LITTLE PUFFERS

A Guide to
Britain's Narrow Gauge
Railways
2019-2020

EDITOR
Steve Askew

Fifteenth Edition

RAILWAY LOCATOR MAP

The numbers shown on this map relate to the page numbers for each railway. Pages 5-6 contain an alphabetical listing of the railways featured in this guide. Please note that the markers on this map show the approximate location only.

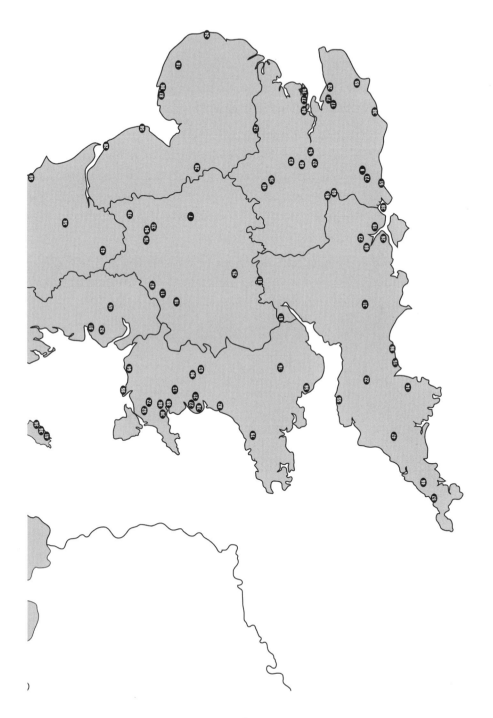

3

ACKNOWLEDGEMENTS

We were greatly impressed by the friendly and cooperative manner of the staff and helpers of the railways which we selected to appear in this book, and wish to thank them all for the help they have given. In addition we wish to thank Bob Budd (cover design), Michael Robinson (page layouts) and Jonathan James (who provided a number of photographs) for their help.

For this edition of *Little Puffers*, we have decided to continue to include, as a separate section, the country's three leading Heritage Tramways.

Although we believe that the information contained in this guide is accurate at the time of going to press, we, and the Railways and Museums itemised, are unable to accept liability for any loss, damage, distress or injury suffered as a result of any inaccuracies. Furthermore, we and the Railways are unable to guarantee operating and opening times which may always be subject to cancellation without notice, particularly during adverse weather conditions.

If you feel we should include other locations or information in future editions, please let us know so that we may give them consideration. We would like to thank you for buying this guide and wish you 'Happy Railway Travelling'!

Steve Askew

EDITOR

British Library Cataloguing in Publication Data
A catalogue record for this book is available from the British Library

ISBN-13:   978-1-86223-399-7

Copyright © 2019, SOCCER BOOKS LIMITED. (01472 696226)
72 St. Peter's Avenue, Cleethorpes, N.E. Lincolnshire, DN35 8HU, England

Manufactured in the UK by TJ International Ltd.

FOREWORD

For the purposes of this publication, we define railways solely by their gauge and include only those with a gauge in excess of 7¼ inches but less than UK Standard gauge. We also publish 'Still Steaming', a separate guide for Standard gauge railways and 'Tiny Trains', a guide for railways with gauges of 7¼ inches and smaller. Both of these guides, as well as further copies of 'Little Puffers' can be ordered UK post free from the Soccer Books Limited address opposite.

The cover photograph shows 0-4-0 locomotive 'Effie' operating on the Cleethorpes Coast Light Railway during September 2018.

CONTENTS

Locator Map (North) 2
Locator Map (South) 3
Acknowledgments 4
Foreword and Contents 5-6
Abbey Pumping Station 7
Almond Valley Light Railway 8
Amberley Museum & Heritage Centre 9
Amerton Railway 10
Apedale Valley Light Railway 11
Audley End Steam Railway 12
Bala Lake Railway 13
Bickington Steam Railway 14
Bicton Woodland Railway 15
Brecon Mountain Railway 16
Bredgar & Wormshill Light Railway 17
Bure Valley Railway 18
Bursledon Brickworks Museum 19
Cleethorpes Coast Light Railway 20
The Corris Railway 21
Devon Railway Centre 22
Eastleigh Lakeside Railway 23
East Suffolk Light Railway 24
Evesham Vale Light Railway 25
Exbury Gardens Railway 26
Fairbourne Railway 27
Faversham Miniature Railway 28
Ferry Meadows Miniature Railway 29
Ffestiniog Railway 30
Gartell Light Railway 31
Giant's Causeway & Bushmills Railway 32
Golden Valley Light Railway 33
Great Laxey Mine Railway 34
Great Whipsnade Railway 35
Groudle Glen Railway 36
Hampton & Kempton Waterworks Railway 37
Hastings Miniature Railway 38
Hayling Railway 39
Heatherslaw Light Railway 40
Isle of Man Steam Railway 41

Kerr's Miniature Railway 42

Kirklees Light Railway 43

Lakeshore Railroad 44

Lancashire Mining Museum 45

Lappa Valley Steam Railway 46

Launceston Steam Railway 47

Leadhills & Wanlockhead Railway 48

Leighton Buzzard Railway 49

Lincolnshire Coast Light Railway 50

Littlehampon Railway 51

Llanberis Lake Railway 52

Locomotion 53

London Museum of Water & Steam 54

Lynton & Barnstaple Railway 55

Margam Park Railway 56

Moseley Industrial Narrow Gauge Tramway, Toy & Mining Museum 57

National Railway Museum 58

North Bay Miniature Railway 59

Old Kiln Light Railway 60

Perrygrove Railway 61

Ravenglass & Eskdale Railway 62

Rhiw Valley Light Railway 63

Rhyl Miniature Railway 64

Romney, Hythe & Dymchurch Railway 65

Royal Victoria Railway 66

Rudyard Lake Steam Railway 67

Ruislip Lido Railway 68

Saltburn Miniature Railway 69

Sherwood Forest Railway 70

Sittingbourne & Kemsley Light Railway 71

Snowdon Mountain Railway 72

South Downs Light Railway 73

Southend Pier Railway 74

South Tynedale Railway 75

Steeple Grange Light Railway 76

Sutton Hall Railway 77

Talyllyn Railway 78

Teifi Valley Railway 79

Threlkeld Quarry Railway 80

Toddington Narrow Gauge Railway 81

Vale of Rheidol Railway 82

Watford Miniature Railway 83

Wat Tyler Miniature Railway 84

Wellington Country Park Railway 85

Wells Harbour Railway 86

Wells & Walsingham Light Railway 87

Welsh Highland Heritage Railway 88

Welsh Highland Railway (now part of the Ffestiniog Railway) 89

Welshpool & Llanfair Light Railway 90

West Lancashire Light Railway 91

Windmill Animal Farm Railway 92

Woodhorn Narrow Gauge Railway 93

Crich Tramway Village 94

Great Orme Tramway 95

Seaton Tramway 96

ABBEY PUMPING STATION

Address: Abbey Pumping Station Museum, Corporation Road, Leicester, LE4 5PX **Telephone Nº**: (0116) 299-5111 **Year Formed**: 1974 **Location of Line**: Leicester **Length of Line**: 300 yards	**Nº of Steam Locos**: 1 **Nº of Other Locos**: 4 **Nº of Members**: Approximately 140 **Annual Membership Fee**: £8.00 Adult **Approx Nº of Visitors P.A.**: 60,000 **Gauge**: 2 feet **Web site**: www.abbeypumpingstation.org

GENERAL INFORMATION

Nearest Mainline Station: Leicester London Road (3 miles)
Nearest Bus Station: Leicester (1½ miles)
Car Parking: Free parking available on site (£3.00 for parking at the Space Centre on Special Event days)
Coach Parking: Use the Space Centre car park
Souvenir Shop(s): Yes
Food & Drinks: Available on special event days only

SPECIAL INFORMATION

The Museum is situated in the Abbey Pumping Station which, from 1891 to 1964 pumped Leicester's sewage to nearby treatment works. The Museum now collects and displays the industrial, technological and scientific heritage of Leicester and contains rare working examples of Woolf compound rotative beam engines which are in steam on selected days.

OPERATING INFORMATION

Opening Times: The Pumping Station is open daily from February to October, 11.00am to 4.30pm, except for Special Event Days when times may vary. Trains run on the dates detailed below.
Steam Working: Selected Special Event days only. 2019 dates: 23rd & 27th April; 5th & 28th May; 1st, 22nd & 23rd June; 6th July; 3rd & 13th August; 8th September; 5th, 15th & 26th October; 30th November; 8th December; 2nd February 2020.
Prices: Admission to the museum is free of charge except for Special Event Days. Prices vary on these dates so please check the web site for further details.

Detailed Directions by Car:
From All Parts: The Museum is situated next to the National Space Centre, about 1 mile North of Leicester city centre near Beaumont Leys and Belgrave. Brown tourist signs with a distinctive rocket logo provide directions to the NSC from the arterial routes around Leicester and the Museum is nearby.

ALMOND VALLEY LIGHT RAILWAY

Address: Almond Valley Heritage Centre, Millfield, Livingston EH54 7AR
Telephone N⁰: (01506) 414957
Year Formed: 1993
Location of Line: Livingston
Length of Line: 550 yards

N⁰ of Steam Locos: None
N⁰ of Other Locos: 3
Approx N⁰ of Visitors P.A.: 125,000
Gauge: 2 feet 6 inches
Web site: www.almondvalley.co.uk

GENERAL INFORMATION

Nearest Mainline Station: Livingston North (1 mile)
Nearest Bus Station: Livingston (1 mile)
Car Parking: Available on site
Coach Parking: Available
Souvenir Shop(s): Yes
Food & Drinks: Available

SPECIAL INFORMATION

The railway runs through the grounds of the Almond Valley Heritage Centre which hosts a wide range of other attractions including a farm, a historic Mill, nature trails and picnic areas.

OPERATING INFORMATION

Opening Times: The Centre is open daily from 10.00am to 5.00pm throughout the year except on 25th & 26th December and 1st & 2nd January. The railway operates at weekends between Easter and the end of September, and daily during some holiday periods, from 11.00am to 4.00pm. Please contact Almond Valley for further details.
Steam Working: None at present.
Prices: Adults £8.50 (Admission to Centre)
Children £6.50 (Admission to Centre)
Senior Citizen £6.50 (Admission to Centre)
Note: Train rides are an extra £1.00 per person.

Detailed Directions by Car:
From All Parts: Exit the M8 at Junction 3A and take the A779 towards Livingston. Almond Valley Heritage Centre is located near the junction of the A779 and the A705 and is clearly signposted.

AMBERLEY MUSEUM

Address: Amberley Museum, Amberley, Arundel BN18 9LT **Telephone Nº**: (01798) 831370 **E-mail**: office@amberleymuseum.co.uk **Year Formed**: 1979 **Location of Line**: Amberley **Length of Line**: ¾ mile	**Nº of Steam Locos**: 3 **Nº of Other Locos**: 20+ **Nº of Members**: 300 volunteers **Annual Membership Fee**: £35.00 **Approx Nº of Visitors P.A.**: 50,000 **Gauge**: 2 feet **Web site**: www.amberleymuseum.co.uk

GENERAL INFORMATION

Nearest Mainline Station: Amberley (adjacent)
Nearest Bus Station: –
Car Parking: Free parking available on site
Coach Parking: Free parking available on site
Souvenir Shop(s): Yes
Food & Drinks: Yes

SPECIAL INFORMATION

Amberley Museum covers 36 acres of former chalk pits and comprises over 40 buildings containing hundreds of different exhibits. There is plenty to see in all weathers and dogs are welcome.

OPERATING INFORMATION

Opening Times: 2019 dates: Wednesday to Sunday from 6th March to 3rd November and also on Bank Holiday Mondays. Trains operate from approximately 11.00am until 4.00pm.
The Museum itself is open from 10.00am to 4.30pm.
Steam Working: Please phone or check the web site for details.
Prices: Adult £15.00
Child £8.00 (free for Under-4's)
Concessions £13.00

Detailed Directions by Car:
From All Parts: Amberley Museum is situated in West Sussex on the B2139 mid-way between Arundel and Storrington and is adjacent to Amberley Railway Station.

AMERTON RAILWAY

Address: Amerton Railway, Stow-by-Chartley, Staffordshire ST18 0LA
Telephone Nº: (01889) 271337
Year Formed: 1991
Location: Amerton Railway
Length of Line: Approximately 1 mile

Nº of Steam Locos: 4 (+1 in restoration)
Nº of Other Locos: 6 (+2 in restoration)
Nº of Members: 90
Approx Nº of Visitors P.A.: 30,000
Gauge: 2 feet
Web site: www.amertonrailway.co.uk

GENERAL INFORMATION

Nearest Mainline Station: Stafford (8 miles)
Nearest Bus Station: Stafford (8 miles)
Car Parking: Free parking available on site
Coach Parking: Available by arrangement
Souvenir Shop(s): Yes
Food & Drinks: Yes

SPECIAL INFORMATION

The railway operates both locomotives and rolling stock which were built in Staffordshire. The Summer Steam Gala in 2019 will be held on 29th & 30th June with the Everything Goes Gala on 14th & 15th September.

OPERATING INFORMATION

Opening Times: 2019 dates: Weekends from the 6th April to 3rd November and daily during the School Holidays. Santa Specials run on weekends from 30th November to 24th December. Open from 11.30am to 4.30pm at weekends but only until 4.00pm during midweek dates.
Steam Working: Sundays and Bank Holidays plus a Steam Gala in June. Please contact the railway for further information.
Prices: Adult £2.50   Child £1.80
             Concession £2.00
E-mail: enquiries@amertonrailway.co.uk

Detailed Directions by Car:
Amerton is located on the A518, 1 mile from the junction with the A51 – Amerton Farm is signposted at the junction. The Railway is located approximately 8 miles from Junction 14 of the M6.

APEDALE VALLEY LIGHT RAILWAY

Address: Apedale Valley Country Park, Chesterton, Newcastle-under-Lyme	**Nº of Steam Locos:** 4
Telephone Nº: 0845 094-1953	**Nº of Other Locos:** 76
Year Formed: 1969	**Nº of Members:** 200+
Location: Apedale Valley Community Country Park	**Annual Membership Fee:** £19.00
Length of Line: ¼ mile	**Gauge:** 2 feet
	Web site: www.avlr.org.uk

GENERAL INFORMATION

Nearest Mainline Station: Longport (2 miles)
Nearest Bus Station: Hanley (3½ miles)
Car Parking: Available
Coach Parking: Available
Souvenir Shop(s): Yes
Food & Drinks: Available

SPECIAL INFORMATION

The Apedale Valley Light Railway is operated by the Moseley Railway Trust (www.mrt.org.uk).

OPERATING INFORMATION

Opening Times: 2019 dates: Every weekend and Bank Holiday from 6th April to 27th October. Santa Specials run on some December weekends. Trains usually run from 11.30am to 4.00pm. Please contact the railway or check the web site for further details.
Steam Working: Special Event days, Bank Holiday weekends plus the second weekend in each month. Special Events to be held in 2019 include 'Swords to Ploughshares' on 29th & 30th July and a celebration of the 50th Anniversary of the Moseley Railway Trust on 21st & 22nd September.
Prices: Adult £3.00   Child £1.50
Note: Different prices may apply for special events.

Detailed Directions by Car:
Exit the M6 at Junction 16 and take the A500 to the A34 and head southwards. Turn right at the traffic island by the McDonald's restaurant and follow the brown tourist signs for Apedale Valley. Follow Loomer Road in Chesterton to the end and continue into the Park. Use the car park at the Heritage Centre as there is no direct access to the railway by car. SatNav: Use ST5 7LB. This postcode is the speedway track on the approach to the park. Continue past the speedway track and continue along Loomer Road for the park.

AUDLEY END STEAM RAILWAY

Address: Audley End, Saffron Walden, Essex CB11 4JB	**Length of Line**: 1½ miles
Telephone Nº: (01799) 510726	**Nº of Steam Locos**: 5
Year Formed: 1964	**Nº of Other Locos**: 2
Location of Line: Opposite Audley End House, Saffron Walden	**Approx Nº of Visitors P.A.**: 42,000
	Gauge: 10¼ inches
	Web site: www.audley-end-railway.co.uk

GENERAL INFORMATION

Nearest Mainline Station: Audley End (1 mile)
Nearest Bus Station: Saffron Walden (1 mile)
Car Parking: Available on site
Coach Parking: Available on site
Souvenir Shop(s): Yes
Food & Drinks: Available in the Cafe

SPECIAL INFORMATION

Audley End Steam Railway is Lord Braybrooke's private miniature railway situated just next to Audley End House, an English Heritage site. Private parties can be catered for outside of normal running hours.

OPERATING INFORMATION

Opening Times: 2019 dates: Weekends and Bank Holidays from 23rd March to 29th September, daily from 6th July to 8th September and during other School Holidays. Santa Specials operate on 23rd, 24th & 25th November and 1st, 7th, 8th and 14th to 24th December. Trains run from 10.30pm until 3.30pm except on Special Event days. Please check the web site for further information.
Steam Working: Most operating days.
Prices: Adult £8.00
              Child £7.00 (Under-2s ride free)
Note: Additional rides can be purchased on the day for £2.00. Different prices may apply for Special Event days.

Detailed Directions by Car:
Exit the M11 at Junction 10 if southbound or Junction 9 if northbound and follow the signs for Audley End House. The railway is situated just across the road from Audley End House.

BALA LAKE RAILWAY

Address: Bala Lake Railway, Llanuwchllyn, Gwynedd, LL23 7DD **Telephone Nº**: (01678) 540666 **Year Formed**: 1972 **Location of Line**: Llanuwchllyn to Bala **Length of Line**: 4½ miles	**Nº of Steam Locos**: 7 (6 in service) **Nº of Other Locos**: 6 **Approx Nº of Visitors P.A.**: 26,000 **Gauge**: 1 foot 11 five-eighth inches **Web site**: www.bala-lake-railway.co.uk **E-mail**: enquiries@bala-lake-railway.co.uk

GENERAL INFORMATION

Nearest Mainline Station: Wrexham (40 miles)
Nearest Bus Station: Wrexham (40 miles)
Car Parking: Adequate parking in Llanuwchllyn
Coach Parking: At Llanuwchllyn or in Bala Town Centre
Souvenir Shop(s): Yes
Food & Drinks: Yes – unlicensed!

SPECIAL INFORMATION

Bala Lake Railway is a narrow-gauge railway which follows 4½ miles of the former Ruabon to Barmouth G.W.R. line.

OPERATING INFORMATION

Opening Times: 2019 dates: 2nd April to 29th September but closed on Mondays and Fridays (excepting Bank Holidays and School Holidays) in April, May, June and September. Also open on dates during October.
Steam Working: All advertised services are steam hauled. Trains run from 11.00am to 3.55pm.
Prices: Adult Single £7.50;   Return £11.50
           Child Single £3.50;   Return £5.50
           Senior Citizen Return £10.50
Family Tickets (Return): £13.50 (1 Adult + 1 Child); £27.00 (2 Adults + 2 Children).
Additional Children are charged £3.00 each.
Under-3s travel free of charge.
Dogs travel for £1.00 (Guide dogs free of charge)

Detailed Directions by Car:
From All Parts: The railway is situated ½ mile off the A494 Bala to Dolgellau road which is accessible from the A470 and via the national motorway network. Follow the brown tourist signs from Llanuwchllyn or Bala.

Bickington Steam Railway

Address: Trago Mills Shopping & Leisure Centre, Stover, Devon TQ12 6JB	**Nº of Steam Locos:** 4
Telephone Nº: (01626) 821111	**Nº of Other Locos:** 1
Year Formed: 1988	**Approx Nº of Visitors P.A.:** Not known
Location of Line: Near the junction of A38 and A382	**Gauge:** 10¼ inches
Length of Line: 2½ miles	**Web site:** bickingtonrailway.wixsite.com/bickington-railway

GENERAL INFORMATION

Nearest Mainline Station: Newton Abbott (3½ miles)
Nearest Bus Station: Newton Abbott
Car Parking: Free parking available on site
Coach Parking: Available on site
Souvenir Shop(s): Yes
Food & Drinks: Available adjacent to the Railway

SPECIAL INFORMATION

Bickington Steam Railway is part of the Trago Mills Shopping & Leisure Centre. The site has numerous other attractions including, 'The Finest 00-gauge Model Railway in the UK'!

OPERATING INFORMATION

Opening Times: 2019: Weekends and Bank Holidays throughout the year then daily from the last week of May to the last week of September and during other School Holidays. Also open for Santa Specials from 1st to 22nd December. Trains run from 11.00am on operating days.
Steam Working: Most operating days but please contact the Railway for precise information.
Prices: Adults £2.00
        Children £1.50 (Under-4s free)
        Senior Citizens £1.50

Detailed Directions by Car:
From All Parts: Take the M5 from Exeter to the A38 and head towards Plymouth. Exit at the junction with the A382 and follow the signs for 'Trago Mills'. The railway is approximately 1 mile. (SatNav use TQ12 6JD)

BICTON WOODLAND RAILWAY

Address: Bicton Woodland Railway, Bicton Park Botanical Gardens, East Budleigh, Budleigh Salterton   EX9 7OP
Telephone Nº: (01395) 568465
Year Formed: 1963
Location of Line: Bicton Gardens
Length of Line: 1½ miles

Nº of Steam Locos: None at present
Nº of Other Locos: 2
Nº of Members: 5,000+
Annual Membership Fee: From £20.95
Approx Nº of Visitors P.A.: 300,000
Gauge: 1 foot 6 inches
Web site: www.bictongardens.co.uk

GENERAL INFORMATION

Nearest Railtrack Station: Exmouth (6 miles)
Nearest Bus Station: Exeter (14 miles)
Car Parking: Free parking at site
Coach Parking: Free parking at site
Souvenir Shop(s): Yes
Food & Drinks: Yes

SPECIAL INFORMATION

The railway runs through the grounds of Bicton Park Botanical Gardens which span over 60 acres. The railway is the only 18 inch gauge line in the UK.

OPERATING INFORMATION

Opening Times: Daily 10.00am to 5.30pm during the Summer and 10.00am to 4.30pm during the Winter. Closed on Christmas Day and Boxing Day.
Steam Working: None at present
Prices: Adult £11.95 (Entrance);   £2.00 (Rides)
        Child £9.95 (Entrance);   £1.70 (Rides)
Concessions £10.95 (Entrance);   £1.90 (Rides)
Note: Under-2s ride for free and entrance tickets for the gardens purchased online are cheaper.

Detailed Directions by Car:
From All Parts: Exit the M5 motorway at Exeter services, Junction 30 and follow the brown tourist signs to Bicton Park.   For SATNAV to the railway, please use the following postcode: EX9 7BG

BRECON MOUNTAIN RAILWAY

Address: Pant Station, Merthyr Tydfil, CF48 2DD	**Gauge**: 1 foot 11¾ inches
Telephone Nº: (01685) 722988	**Length of Line**: 5 miles
Year Formed: 1980	**Nº of Steam Locos**: 8
Location of Line: North of Merthyr Tydfil – 1 mile from the A465	**Nº of Other Locos**: 3
	Approx Nº of Visitors P.A.: 75,000
	Web site: www.bmr.wales

GENERAL INFORMATION

Nearest Mainline Station: Merthyr Tydfil (3 miles)
Nearest Bus Station: Merthyr Tydfil (3 miles)
Car Parking: Free parking available at Pant Station
Coach Parking: Free parking available at Pant Station
Souvenir Shop(s): Yes
Food & Drinks: Yes – including licensed Tea Rooms

SPECIAL INFORMATION

It is possible to take a break before the return journey at Pontsticill to have a picnic, take a forest walk, visit the lakeside snackbar and play area or visit the new Steam Museum.

OPERATING INFORMATION

Opening Times: Weekends and Bank Holidays throughout the year and daily during School holidays. Daily from February to the end of October but closed on some Mondays and Fridays in April, May, September and October. Open almost every day in December for Santa Specials. Trains typically run from 10.30am to 3.45pm and from 10.30pm to 2.30pm during off-peak times.
Steam Working: Most services are steam hauled.
Prices: Adults £15.00
          Children £7.50 (Ages 2 and under ride free)
          Senior Citizens £13.50
Note: Two children can travel for £6.25 each when accompanying a paying adult.

Detailed Directions by Car:
Exit the M4 at Junction 32 and take the A470 to Merthyr Tydfil. Go onto the A465 and follow the brown tourist signs for the railway. SATNAV users should enter the following postcode: CF48 2DD

BREDGAR & WORMSHILL LIGHT RAILWAY

Address: The Warren, Bredgar, near Sittingbourne, Kent ME9 8AT
Telephone Nº: (01622) 884254
Year Formed: 1972
Location of Line: 1 mile south of Bredgar
Length of Line: ¾ mile

Gauge: 2 feet
Nº of Steam Locos: 10
Nº of Other Locos: 11
Approx Nº of Visitors P.A.: 7,000
Web site: www.bwlr.co.uk

GENERAL INFORMATION

Nearest Mainline Station: Sittingbourne (5 miles)
Nearest Bus Station: Sittingbourne
Car Parking: 500 spaces available – free parking
Coach Parking: Free parking available by appointment
Souvenir Shop(s): Yes   **Food & Drinks**: Yes

SPECIAL INFORMATION

A small but beautiful railway in rural Kent. The railway also has other attractions including a Model Railway, Traction Engines, a Beam Engine, Vintage cars and tractors, a Locomotive Shed, a picnic site and woodland walks.

OPERATING INFORMATION

Opening Times: 2019 dates: Open on Easter Sunday then the first Sunday of the month from May to October and on Sunday 27th October. Trains run from 11.00am to 4.30pm.
Steam Working: Every operating day.
Prices: Adult £12.50
              Child £5.00 (Under-4s travel free)
              Family Ticket £30.00
                      (2 adults + 3 children)
Note: The prices shown above include parking and unlimited rides on the day of purchase.

Detailed Directions by Car:
Take the M20 and exit at Junction 8 (Leeds Castle exit). Travel 4½ miles due north through Hollingbourne. The Railway is situated a little over 1 mile south of Bredgar village.

BURE VALLEY RAILWAY

Address: Aylsham Station, Norwich Road, Aylsham, Norfolk NR11 6BW	**Nº of Steam Locos**: 5
Telephone Nº: (01263) 733858	**Nº of Other Locos**: 3
Year Formed: 1989	**Approx Nº of Visitors P.A.**: 120,000
Location of Line: Aylsham to Wroxham	**Gauge**: 15 inches
Length of Line: 9 miles	**Web Site**: www.bvrw.co.uk
	e-mail: info@bvrw.co.uk

GENERAL INFORMATION

Nearest Mainline Station: Hoveton & Wroxham (adjacent)
Nearest Bus Station: Aylsham (bus passes station)
Car Parking: Free parking for passengers at Aylsham and Wroxham Stations
Coach Parking: As above
Souvenir Shop(s): Yes at both Stations
Food & Drinks: Yes (Café at Aylsham opens daily)

SPECIAL INFORMATION

Boat trains connect at Wroxham with a 1½ hour cruise on the Norfolk Broads National Park. Steam Locomotive driving courses are available throughout the year except in July and August. All trains have carriages which are able to carry wheelchairs.

OPERATING INFORMATION

Opening Times: Aylsham Station is open daily. Trains run on various dates in 2019 including weekends in March and daily from 30th March to 31st October, plus some other dates. Trains run from 10.00am to 5.25pm during high season. Open for Santa Specials on weekends and other dates in November and December. Trains also operate during the February half-term. Please contact the railway for further details.
Steam Working: Most trains are steam hauled
Prices: Adult Return £14.00   (Single £9.00)
 Child Return £7.00   (Single £5.50)
 Family Return £37.00   (2 adult + 2 child)
Party discounts are available for groups of 20 or more if booked in advance.

Detailed Directions by Car:
From Norwich: Aylsham Station is situated midway between Norwich and Cromer on the A140 – follow the signs for Aylsham Town Centre. Wroxham Station is adjacent to the Wroxham British Rail Station – take the A1151 from Norwich; From King's Lynn: Take the A148 and B1354 to reach Aylsham Station.
Satellite Navigation: Use NR11 6BW for Aylsham Station and NR12 8UU for Wroxham Station.

BURSLEDON BRICKWORKS MUSEUM

Address: Swanwick Lane, Swanwick, Southampton SO31 7HB
Telephone Nº: (01489) 576248
Year Formed: 1994 (Railway established in 2010)
Location of Line: Bursledon Brickworks
Length of Line: A third of a mile

Nº of Steam Locos: 2
Nº of Other Locos: 2
Approx Nº of Visitors P.A.: 8,000
Gauge: 2 feet and 7¼ inches
Web site: www.hngrt.org.uk

GENERAL INFORMATION

Nearest Mainline Station: Bursledon (¾ mile)
Nearest Bus Station: Southampton
Car Parking: Available on site
Coach Parking: Available on site
Souvenir Shop(s): On site
Food & Drinks: Available

SPECIAL INFORMATION

The 2 foot gauge railway is operated by the Hampshire Narrow Gauge Railway Trust which owns 2 steam locomotives and 2 heritage petrol-driven locomotives.

OPERATING INFORMATION

Opening Times: Wednesdays, Thursdays and Sundays from April to late October. 11.00am to 4.00pm.
Steam Working: 2019 dates: 28th April; 26th May; 23rd June; 21st July; 18th August; 15th, 22nd & 29th September; 27th October; 24th November.
Prices: Adults £5.00 (£7.00 on Special Event days)
Children £3.00 (£4.00 Steam Event days)
Concessions £4.00 (£6.00 Special Events)
Family £13.00 (£18.00 on Special Events)
Note: There is a small additional charge for train rides which are subject to availability.

Detailed Directions by Car:
Exit the M27 at Junction 8 and take the A3024 towards Bursledon. Take the first exit at the roundabout onto the A27 Bridge Road, passing Bursledon on the right before turning left into Swanwick Lane after crossing the River Hamble. The Brickworks is on the left from Swanwick Lane, situated alongside the M27.

CLEETHORPES COAST LIGHT RAILWAY

Address: King's Road, Cleethorpes, North East Lincolnshire   DN35 0AG
Telephone Nº: (01472) 604657
Year Formed: 1948
Location of Line: Lakeside Park & Marine embankment along Cleethorpes seafront
Length of Line: 2 miles

Nº of Steam Locos: 9
Nº of Other Locos: 5
Gauge: 15 inches
Web site: www.cclr.co.uk
E-mail: info@cclr.co.uk

GENERAL INFORMATION

Nearest Mainline Station: Cleethorpes (1 mile)
Nearest Bus Stop: Meridian Point (opposite)
Car Parking: Boating Lake car park – 500 spaces (fee charged)
Coach Parking: As above
Souvenir Shop(s): Yes
Food & Drinks: Platform One Café and The Signal Box Inn, described as 'The Smallest Pub on the Planet', are both located at Lakeside Station.

OPERATING INFORMATION

Opening Times: 2019 dates: Open daily from 30th March to 6th October and during local School Holidays from February to October. Also open at weekends February to December. Trains run from 10.00am on most days. Please check the website for further details.
Steam Working: Most services are steam hauled.
Prices: Adult Return £5.00   Child Return £4.00
           Family Return £16.00   (2 Adult + 2 Child)

Detailed Directions by Car:
Take the M180 to the A180 and continue to its' end. Follow signs for Cleethorpes. The Railway is situated along Cleethorpes seafront 1 mile to the south of the Pier. Look for the brown tourist signs marked Meridian Lakeside and the main station is adjacent to the Leisure Centre.

THE CORRIS RAILWAY

Address: Station Yard, Corris, Machynlleth, Mid Wales SY20 9SH
Telephone Nº: (01654) 761303
Year Formed: 1966
Location of Line: Corris to Maespoeth, Mid Wales
Length of Line: ¾ mile

Nº of Steam Locos: 1
Nº of Other Locos: 5
Nº of Members: 500
Annual Membership Fee: £22.00 (adult)
Approx Nº of Visitors P.A.: 7,000
Gauge: 2 feet 3 inches
Web site: www.corris.co.uk
E-mail: enquiries@corris.co.uk

GENERAL INFORMATION

Nearest Mainline Station: Machynlleth (5 miles)
Nearest Bus Station: Machynlleth (5 miles)
Car Parking: Available on site and also at the Corris Craft Centre (500 yards)
Coach Parking: Corris Craft Centre (please pre-book if visiting)
Souvenir Shop(s): Yes
Food & Drinks: Yes

SPECIAL INFORMATION

The Corris Railway originally ran from 1859 to 1948. A second steam locomotive and two carriages are being built and work on an extension to the partly-rebuilt line is currently underway.

OPERATING INFORMATION

Opening Times: 2019 dates: Open during Easter Weekend then every Sunday from 5th May to 27th October and Saturdays from 13th July to the end of August, Mondays and Tuesdays during August, on all Bank Holiday weekends and on 26th October. Santa Specials run on 7th & 8th December. The first train leaves Corris Station at 11.00am, the last train leaves at 4.00pm.
Steam Working: Most trains are steam-hauled.
Prices: Adult Return £6.00
Child Return £3.00 (Ages 5 to 15)
Senior Citizen Return £5.50
Family Return £15.00
(2 adults + 2 children)

Detailed Directions by Car:
From All Parts: Corris is situated off the A487, five miles north of Machynlleth and 11 miles south of Dolgellau. Turn off the trunk road at the Braichgoch Bunkhouse & Inn and the Station Yard is the 2nd turning on the right as you enter the village, just past the Holy Trinity Church.

DEVON RAILWAY CENTRE

Address: Bickleigh, Tiverton, Devon, EX16 8RG	**Nº of Steam Locos:** 1
Telephone Nº: (01884) 855671	**Nº of Other Locos:** 12
Year Formed: 1997	**Approx Nº of Visitors P.A.:** Not recorded
Location of Line: Bickleigh, Devon	**Gauge:** 2 feet, 7¼ inches and Standard
Length of Line: ½ mile (2 foot and 7¼ inch gauges); 200 yards (Standard gauge)	**Web site:** www.devonrailwaycentre.co.uk
	E-mail: devonrailway@btinternet.com

GENERAL INFORMATION

Nearest Mainline Station: Exeter
Nearest Bus Station: Tiverton (Route 55)
Car Parking: Available on site
Coach Parking: Available on site
Souvenir Shop(s): Yes
Food & Drinks: Yes

SPECIAL INFORMATION

Devon Railway Centre has passenger carrying lines and also features a large model railway exhibition with 15 working layouts. A delightful Edwardian model village built to a 1:12 scale has recently been extended with a model funfair added and a new museum coach opened recently.

OPERATING INFORMATION

Opening Times: 2019 dates: Daily from 6th to 28th April, 22nd May to 8th September and 19th to 27th October. Closed on Mondays in June. Open Wednesday to Sunday inclusive from 1st to 26th May and 11th to 29th September. Also open during weekends in October. Open from 10.30am until 5.00pm on all operating days.
Steam Working: Please phone or e-mail for details.
Prices: Adult £8.80   Child £7.80
    Senior Citizen £8.00   Family £31.20
Admission includes unlimited train rides and access to the model village, model railways, museum and crazy golf.

Detailed Directions by Car:
From All Parts: Devon Railway Centre is situated adjacent to the famous Bickleigh Bridge, just off the A396 Exeter to Tiverton road (3 miles from Tiverton and 8 miles from Exeter).

EASTLEIGH LAKESIDE STEAM RAILWAY

Address: Lakeside Country Park, Wide Lane, Eastleigh, Hants. SO50 5PE
Telephone Nº: (023) 8061-2020
Year Formed: 1992
Location: Opposite Southampton airport
Length of Line: 1¼ miles

Nº of Steam Locos: 21
Nº of Other Locos: 3
Approx Nº of Visitors P.A.: 50,000
Gauge: 10¼ inches and 7¼ inches
Web site: www.steamtrain.co.uk

GENERAL INFORMATION

Nearest Mainline Station: Southampton Airport (Parkway) (¼ mile)
Nearest Bus Station: Eastleigh (1½ miles)
Car Parking: Free parking available on site
Coach Parking: Free parking available on site
Souvenir Shop(s): Yes
Food & Drinks: Cafe on site is open all year round from 9.00am to 4.00pm.

SPECIAL INFORMATION

The railway also has a playground and picnic area overlooking the lakes.

OPERATING INFORMATION

Opening Times: Weekends throughout the year and daily during school holidays. Open 10.00am to 4.30pm (until 4.00pm during the winter months).
Steam Working: As above
Prices: Adult Return £4.00 (First Class £4.50)
Child Return £3.00 (First Class £3.50)
Tickets are available offering 3 return journeys at reduced rates. Annual season tickets are available.
Children under the age of 2 years ride free of charge.
Driver training courses can be booked in advance.

Detailed Directions by Car:
From All Parts: Exit the M27 at Junction 5 and take the A335 to Eastleigh. The Railway is situated ¼ mile past Southampton Airport Station on the left hand side of the A335.

EAST SUFFOLK LIGHT RAILWAY

Address: East Anglia Transport Museum, Chapel Road, Carlton Colville, Lowestoft   NR33 8BL
Telephone Nº: (01502) 518459
Year Formed: 1972
Location: 3 miles south of Lowestoft
Length of Line: 200 yards

Nº of Steam Locos: None
Nº of Other Locos: 4
Approx Nº of Visitors P.A.: 18,000
Gauge: 2 feet
Web site: www.eatransportmuseum.co.uk

GENERAL INFORMATION

Nearest Mainline Station: Oulton Broad South (2 miles)
Nearest Bus Station: Lowestoft (3 miles)
Car Parking: Available on site
Coach Parking: Available
Souvenir Shop(s): Yes
Food & Drinks: Available

SPECIAL INFORMATION

The railway is located at the East Anglia Transport Museum which also offers visitors trolleybus and tram rides.

OPERATING INFORMATION

Opening Times: 2019 dates: Sundays, Bank Holidays and Thursdays from April to September, also Saturdays from June to September, Tuesdays and Wednesdays from 23rd July to 4th September and some other dates. Usually open from 12.00pm to 4.30pm except for Special Event days. Please check the web site for further information.
Steam Working: None
Prices: Adults £9.00 (Admission and all rides)
          Children £6.00 (Admission and all rides)
          Concessions £8.00 (Admission and rides)

Detailed Directions by Car:
From All Parts: The East Anglia Transport Museum is clearly signposted by brown tourist signs from the A12, A146, A1117 and A1145.

EVESHAM VALE LIGHT RAILWAY

Address: Evesham Country Park,
Twyford, Evesham   WR11 4DS
Telephone Nº: (01386) 422282
Year Formed: 2002
Location of Line: 1 mile north of Evesham
Length of Line: 1¼ miles

Nº of Steam Locos: 3
Nº of Other Locos: 2
Approx Nº of Visitors P.A.: 50,000
Gauge: 15 inches
Web site: www.evlr.co.uk
E-mail: enquiries@evlr.co.uk

GENERAL INFORMATION

Nearest Mainline Station: Evesham (1 mile)
Nearest Bus Station: Evesham (1½ miles)
Car Parking: Available in the Country Park
Coach Parking: Available in the Country Park
Souvenir Shop(s): Yes
Food & Drinks: Various restaurants and cafés in the
shopping area.

SPECIAL INFORMATION

The railway is situated within the 130 acre Evesham
Country Park which has apple orchards and picnic
areas overlooking the picturesque Vale of Evesham.

OPERATING INFORMATION

Opening Times: Open at weekends throughout the
year and daily during school holidays. Trains run
from 10.30am to 4.30pm.
Please phone for further details.
Steam Working: Daily when trains are running.
Prices: Adult Return £2.70
   Child Return £2.20
   Senior Citizen Return £2.40
Note: Special reduced party rates are available for
groups of 20 or more when booked in advance and
Christmas specials operate during December.

Detailed Directions by Car:
From the North: Exit the M42 at Junction 3 and take the A435 towards Alcester then the A46 to Evesham; From
the South: Exit the M5 at Junction 9 and take the A46 to Evesham; From the West: Exit the M5 at Junction 7 and
take the A44 to Evesham; From the East: Take the A44 from Oxford to Evesham. Upon reaching Evesham, follow
the Brown tourist signs for Evesham Country Park and the railway.

EXBURY GARDENS RAILWAY

Address: Exbury Gardens, Exbury, Near Southampton SO45 1AZ	**Nº of Steam Locos**: 3
	Nº of Other Locos: 1
Telephone Nº: (02380) 891203	**Approx Nº of Visitors P.A.**: 85,000
Year Formed: 2001	**Gauge**: 12¼ inches
Location of Line: Exbury	**Web site**: www.exbury.co.uk
Length of Line: 1½ miles	

Photograph courtesy of Gavin Clinton

GENERAL INFORMATION

Nearest Mainline Station: Brockenhurst (8 miles)
Nearest Bus Station: Hill Top (2½ miles)
The New Forest Open Tour Bus visits the gardens 8 times a day between 8th July and 10th September.
Car Parking: Free parking available on site
Coach Parking: Free parking available on site
Souvenir Shop(s): Yes
Food & Drinks: Available

SPECIAL INFORMATION

The railway is located in the world famous Rothschild azalea and rhododendron gardens at Exbury in the New Forest. A walk-through exhibition in the Engine Shed recalls the building of the steam railway.

OPERATING INFORMATION

Opening Times: 2019 dates: Daily from the 23rd March to 3rd November. The gardens are open from 10.00am to 5.00pm (or dusk if earlier) and car park gates close at 6.00pm.
Steam Working: Most running days from 11.00am (restricted operation in March and September).
Prices: Adult Return £17.50
　　　　　　 Child Return £9.00   (Under-3s free)
　　　　　　 Family Ticket £49.00 (2 adult + 3 child)
Note: The above prices include admission to the Gardens which is required to visit the railway. Please check the Exbury web site for further details of entrance fees for the Gardens.

Detailed Directions by Car:
From all directions: Exit the M27 at Junction 2 and take the A326 to Dibden. Follow the brown tourist signs for Exbury Gardens & Steam Railway.

FAIRBOURNE RAILWAY

Address: Beach Road, Fairbourne, Dolgellau, Gwynedd LL38 2EX	**Nº of Steam Locos:** 4
Telephone Nº: (01341) 250362	**Nº of Other Locos:** 3
Year Formed: 1916	**Nº of Members:** 400
Location of Line: On A493 between Tywyn & Dolgellau	**Annual Membership Fee:** £25.00
	Approx Nº of Visitors P.A.: 18,000
Length of Line: 2 miles	**Gauge:** 12¼ inches
	Web Site: www.fairbournerailway.com

GENERAL INFORMATION

Nearest Mainline Station: Fairbourne (adjacent)
Nearest Bus Station: Fairbourne (adjacent)
Car Parking: Available in Mainline station car park
Coach Parking: Pay & Display car park 300 yards
Souvenir Shop(s): Yes
Food & Drinks: Yes – licensed Cafes at Fairbourne and Barmouth Ferry Terminus

SPECIAL INFORMATION

There is a connecting ferry service (foot passengers only) from Barmouth to Barmouth Ferry Terminus.

E-mail: office@fairbournerailway.com

OPERATING INFORMATION

Opening Times: 2019 dates: Open daily from 6th April until 3rd November but closed on Mondays and Fridays except during the School Holidays. Santa Specials are planned for 14th and 15th December.

Steam Working: The majority of services are steam-hauled. A special Steam Gala runs on 26th, 27th and 28th May.

Prices: Adult Day Rover £10.50
Unaccompanied Child Day Rover £6.00
(accompanied Children are £1.00 each)
Under-3s ride for free
Dog ticket £1.00

Detailed Directions by Car:
From A470: Follow signs for Dolgellau and turn left onto A493 towards Tywyn. The turn-off for Fairbourne is located 8 miles south-west of Dolgellau; From South Wales: Follow signs for Machynlleth, then follow A487 towards Dolgellau. Then take A493 towards Fairbourne.

FAVERSHAM MINIATURE RAILWAY

Address: Brogdale Farm, Brogdale Road, Faversham, Kent ME13 8XZ	**Nº of Steam Locos**: 6
Telephone Nº: (01795) 474211	**Nº of Other Locos**: 11
Year Formed: 1984	**Nº of Members**: 40
Location of Line: Faversham, Kent	**Annual Membership Fee**: £10.00 Adult, £40.00 Family
Length of Line: Approximately 1¼ miles	**Approx Nº of Visitors P.A.**: 6,000+
Gauge: 9 inches	**Web**: www.favershamminiaturerailway.co.uk

GENERAL INFORMATION

Nearest Mainline Station: Faversham (¾ mile)
Nearest Bus Station: None, but a regular bus service travels to Faversham from Canterbury
Car Parking: Available on site
Coach Parking: Available on site
Souvenir Shop(s): Various shops on site
Food & Drinks: Available

SPECIAL INFORMATION

Faversham Miniature Railway is the only 9 inch gauge railway in the UK which is open to the public.

OPERATING INFORMATION

Opening Times: Sundays and Bank Holiday weekends from early March to November from 11.00am to 4.00pm. Also open for Santa Specials and other Special Events during the year. Please contact the railway for further information.
Steam Working: Special steam days only. Please contact the Railway for further details.
Prices: £1.50 per ride
£2.00 per ride when Steam-hauled
Note: Different prices may apply for Special Events.

Detailed Directions by Car:
Exit the M2 at Junction 5 and take the A251 towards Faversham. After about ½ mile turn left onto the A2 then left again after ¼ mile turning into Brogdale Road for the Farm and Railway.

FERRY MEADOWS MINIATURE RAILWAY

Address: Ham Lane, Nene Park,
Oundle Road, Peterborough   PE2 5UU
Telephone Nº: (01933) 398889
Year Formed: 1978
Location: Ferry Meadows, Nene Park
Length of Line: ½ mile

Nº of Steam Locos: 1
Nº of Other Locos: 2
Approx Nº of Visitors P.A.: 55,000
Gauge: 10¼ inches
Web site: www.ferrymeadowsrailway.co.uk

GENERAL INFORMATION

Nearest Mainline Station: Peterborough (2 miles)
Nearest Bus Station: Peterborough (2 miles)
Car Parking: Available adjacent
Coach Parking: Available adjacent
Souvenir Shop(s): Yes
Food & Drinks: Available

SPECIAL INFORMATION

The railway is situated in the Ferry Meadows area of
Nene Park in which watersports and other leisure
activities are also available.

OPERATING INFORMATION

Opening Times: 2019 dates: Every weekend and
Bank Holiday from 16th February to 27th October
and daily during July and August.
Trains run from 11.30am to 4.30pm.
Steam Working: Every Sunday and some weekdays
during the School Holidays. Please contact the
railway for further details.
Prices: Adult Return £3.00   Adult Single £2.00
                Adult Day Rover £6.00
                Child Return £2.00   Child Single £1.50
                Child Day Rover £4.00

Detailed Directions by Car:
Nene Park is situated on the A605 Oundle Road. Follow the brown tourist signs for Nene Park.

FFESTINIOG RAILWAY

Address: Ffestiniog Railway, Harbour Station, Porthmadog, Gwynedd LL49 9NF
Telephone Nº: (01766) 516000
Year Formed: 1832
Location of Line: Porthmadog to Blaenau Ffestiniog
Length of Line: 13½ miles

Nº of Steam Locos: 12
Nº of Other Locos: 12
Nº of Members: 5,000
Annual Membership Fee: £30.00
Approx Nº of Visitors P.A.: 360,000
Gauge: 1 foot 11½ inches
Web Site: www.festrail.co.uk

GENERAL INFORMATION

Nearest Mainline Station: Blaenau Ffestiniog (interchange) or Minffordd
Nearest Bus Station: Bus stop next to stations at Porthmadog & Blaenau Ffestiniog
Car Parking: Parking available at Porthmadog, Blaenau Ffestiniog, Minffordd and Tan-y-Bwlch
Coach Parking: Available at Porthmadog and Blaenau Ffestiniog
Souvenir Shop(s): Yes   **Food & Drinks**: Yes

SPECIAL INFORMATION

The Railway runs through the spectacular scenery of Snowdonia National Park and the line now links up with the Welsh Highland Railway.

OPERATING INFORMATION

Opening Times: 2019 dates: Daily service from 30th March to 3rd November. A limited service operates in the Winter and Santa Specials run on December dates. Please contact the railway for further details.
Steam Working: Most trains are steam hauled.
Prices: Adult £25.60 (Round-trip return ticket) One child travels free with each adult, additional children travel for half the fare. Reductions are available groups of 20 or more. Cheaper fares are also available for single rides and shorter journeys.
E-mail: enquiries@ffwhr.com

Detailed Directions by Car:
Portmadog is easily accessible from the Midlands – take the M54/A5 to Corwen then the A494 to Bala onto the A4212 to Trawsfynydd and the A470 (becomes the A487 from Maentwrog) to Porthmadog. From Chester take the A55 to Llandudno Junction and the A470 to Blaenau Ffestiniog. Both Stations are well-signposted.

GARTELL LIGHT RAILWAY

Address: Common Lane, Yenston, Templecombe, Somerset   BA8 0NB
Telephone Nº: (01963) 370752
Year Formed: 1991
Location of Line: South of Templecombe
Length of Line: ¾ mile

Nº of Steam Locos: 2
Nº of Other Locos: 3
Approx Nº of Visitors P.A.: 3,000
Gauge: 2 feet
Web site: www.newglr.weebly.com

GENERAL INFORMATION

Nearest Mainline Station: Templecombe (1¼ miles)
Nearest Bus Station: Wincanton
Car Parking: Free parking adjacent to the station
Coach Parking: Adjacent to the station
Souvenir Shop(s): Yes
Food & Drinks: Meals, snacks and drinks available

SPECIAL INFORMATION

Part of the line runs along the track bed of the former Somerset & Dorset Joint Railway. It features a working junction, road crossing and simultaneous departures in the same direction from Pinesway Junction.

OPERATING INFORMATION

Opening Times: 2019 dates: 22nd April (Easter Monday); 6th & 27th May; 30th June; 28th July; 26th August; 29th September and 27th October. Trains depart at 25 minute intervals between 10.30am and 4.20pm.
Steam Working: Every operating day.
Prices: Adult £8.00
          Senior Citizen £7.00
          Child £5.00 (Under-14s)
          Family £22.00 (2 adults + 2 children)
Note: Tickets permit unlimited travel by any train on the day of purchase. Under-3s travel for free.

Detailed Directions by Car:
From All Parts: The Railway is situated off the A357 just south of Templecombe and on open days is clearly indicated by the usual brown tourist signs.

GIANT'S CAUSEWAY & BUSHMILLS RAILWAY

Address: Giant's Causeway Station, Runkerry Road, Bushmills, Co. Antrim, Northern Ireland BT57 8SZ
Telephone N°: (028) 2073-2844
Year Formed: 2002
Location: Between the distillery village of Bushmills and the Giant's Causeway
Length of Line: 2 miles

N° of Steam Locos: 2
N° of Other Locos: 2
N° of Members: None
Approx N° of Visitors P.A.: 50,000
Gauge: 3 feet
Web site: www.freewebs.com/giantscausewayrailway

GENERAL INFORMATION

Nearest Northern Ireland Railway Station: Coleraine/Portrush
Nearest Bus Station: Coleraine/Portrush
Car Parking: Car Park fee at Giant's Causeway Station is refunded upon ticket purchase. By parking at the Bushmills Station and taking the railway expensive parking charges at the Causeway itself can be avoided.
Coach Parking: Available on site
Souvenir Shop(s): Yes
Food & Drinks: At Giant's Causeway Station only

SPECIAL INFORMATION

The railway links the distillery village of Bushmills (open to visitors) to the World Heritage Site of the Giant's Causeway. The railway itself is built on the final two miles of the pioneering hydro-electric tramway which linked the Giant's Causeway to the main railway at Portrush from 1883 to 1949.

OPERATING INFORMATION

Opening Times: Daily in July and August, over St. Patrick's Day weekend and for Easter week. Also open at weekends from Easter to the end of June and in October & September. Trains run from 11.00am.
Steam Working: Please contact the railway for further information.
Prices: Adult Return £5.00   Child Return £3.00
Concession Return £4.00
Family Return £17.50
Note: Group rates are also available.

Detailed Directions by Car:
From Belfast take the M2 to the junction with the A26 (for Antrim, Ballymena and Coleraine). Follow the A26/M2/A26. From Ballymoney onwards Bushmills and the Giant's Causeway are well signposted. The railway is also well signposted in the immediate vicinity.

GOLDEN VALLEY LIGHT RAILWAY

Address: Butterley Station, Ripley, Derbyshire DE5 3QZ
Telephone N°: (01773) 747674
Year Formed: 1987
Location of Line: Butterley, near Ripley
Length of Line: Four-fifths of a mile

N° of Steam Locos: 2
N° of Other Locos: 19
N° of Members: 75
Annual Membership Fee: £20.00
Approx N° of Visitors P.A.: 10,000
Gauge: 2 feet
Web site: www.gvlr.org.uk

GENERAL INFORMATION

Nearest Mainline Station: Alfreton (6 miles)
Nearest Bus Station: Bus stop outside the Station
Car Parking: Free parking at site – ample space
Coach Parking: Free parking at site
Souvenir Shop(s): Yes – at Butterley and Swanwick
Food & Drinks: Yes – both sites

SPECIAL INFORMATION

The Golden Valley Light Railway is part of the Midland Railway – Butterley and runs from the museum site through the country park to Newlands Inn Station close to the Cromford Canal and the pub of the same name.

OPERATING INFORMATION

Opening Times: 2019 dates: Weekends and Bank Holidays from 6th April to 27th October and Tuesday to Friday during the School Holidays. Trains run from 11.50am to 3.30pm (or 4.15pm when the standard gauge line is operating).
Steam Working: None at present.
Prices: Adult £2.50
          Children £1.00 (Under-5s free of charge)
          Dogs 50p (at the guard's discretion)

Detailed Directions by Car:
From All Parts: From the M1 exit at Junction 28 and take the A38 towards Derby. The railway is signposted at the junction with the B6179.

GREAT LAXEY MINE RAILWAY

Address: Laxey Valley Gardens, Laxey, Isle of Man
Telephone Nº: (01624) 862007 (Easter to the end of October only)
Year Formed: 2004
Location of Line: Laxey Valley Gardens
Length of Line: 550 yards

Nº of Steam Locos: 2
Nº of Other Locos: 1
Nº of Members: Approximately 300
Annual Membership Fee: £15.00
Approx Nº of Visitors P.A.: 7,000
Gauge: 19 inches
Web site: www.laxeyminerailway.im

GENERAL INFORMATION

Nearest Mainline Station: Laxey, Manx Electric Railway
Nearest Bus Station: Laxey
Car Parking: Available nearby
Coach Parking: Available nearby
Souvenir Shop(s): Yes
Food & Drinks: There are a number of Cafes nearby

SPECIAL INFORMATION

The Great Laxey Mine Railway is the recently restored surface section of the former mine tramway, the first section of which was opened in 1823. Originally worked by ponies, these were replaced by two steam locomotives in 1877. These engines were scrapped in 1935 but the restored line now uses two working replicas. A few minutes walk from the terminus of the railway is the Lady Isabella water wheel, the largest in the world. The railway itself is operated entirely by volunteers.

OPERATING INFORMATION

Opening Times: 2019 dates: Every Saturday from 6th April until the end of September. A number of Special Event Days are operated throughout the season, details of which are advertised on the railway's web site. Trains run from 11.00am to 4.30pm.
Steam Working: All trains are steam-hauled
Prices: £2.00 per person (Under-3s ride free)

Detailed Directions by Car:
Laxey is situated approximately 8 miles to the north east of Douglas on the A2 coast road.

GREAT WHIPSNADE RAILWAY (JUMBO EXPRESS)

Address: ZSL Whipsnade Zoo, Dunstable LU6 2LF	**Nº of Steam Locos:** 2
Telephone Nº: (01582) 872171	**Nº of Other Locos:** 5
Year Formed: 1970	**Nº of Members:** None
Location of Line: ZSL Whipsnade Zoo, Near Dunstable	**Approx Nº of Visitors P.A.:** 175,000
	Gauge: 2 feet 6 inches
Length of Line: 1¾ miles	**Web site:** www.zsl.org

GENERAL INFORMATION

Nearest Mainline Station: Luton (7 miles)
Nearest Bus Station: Dunstable (3 miles)
Car Parking: Available just outside the park
Coach Parking: Available just outside the park
Souvenir Shop(s): Next to the Station
Food & Drinks: Available

SPECIAL INFORMATION

The Railway is situated in the ZSL Whipsnade Zoo operated by the Zoological Society of London.

OPERATING INFORMATION

Opening Times: The zoo is open daily from 10.00am throughout the year. Closing time varies from 4.00pm to 6.00pm depending on the time of the year. The railway runs daily from the Easter Holidays until the end of October half-term and at weekends at some other times of the year. Contact the zoo for further details.
Steam Working: Every operating day.
Prices: Adult £28.00
Child £20.95 (Ages 3 to 15 years)
Senior Citizen £25.20
Note: The above prices are for entrance into the Zoo itself and include a voluntary donation. Online bookings are cheaper. Train rides are an extra charge:
Adults £4.50 Children £2.00 Concessions £4.00

Detailed Directions by Car:
From All Parts: Exit the M1 at Junction 11 and take the A505 then the B489. Follow signs for Whipsnade Zoo.

GROUDLE GLEN RAILWAY

Address: Groudle Glen, Onchan, Isle of Man	**Nº of Steam Locos**: 3 **Other Locos**: 3
Telephone Nº: (01624) 670453 (weekends)	**Nº of Members**: 600
Year Formed: 1982 **Re-Opened**: 1986	**Annual Membership Fee**: £15.00 (Adult)
Location of Line: Groudle Glen	**Approx Nº of Visitors P.A.**: 10,000
Length of Line: ¾ mile	**Correspondence**: 29 Hawarden Avenue, Douglas, Isle of Man IM1 4BP
Gauge: 2 feet	**Web site**: www.ggr.org.uk

GENERAL INFORMATION

Nearest Mainline Station: Manx Electric Railway
Nearest Bus Station: Douglas Bus Station
Car Parking: At the entrance to the Glen
Coach Parking: At the entrance to the Glen
Souvenir Shop(s): Yes
Food & Drinks: Coffee and Tea available

SPECIAL INFORMATION

The Railway runs through a picturesque glen to a coastal headland where there are the remains of a Victorian Zoo. The Railway was built in 1896 and closed in 1962. 'Otter', a new steam loco built by North Bay Railway Engineering Works in Darlington, enters service during 2019.

OPERATING INFORMATION

Opening Times: 2019 dates: Easter Sunday and Monday then Sundays from 5th May to 29th September, 11.00am to 4.30pm. Also open on Wednesday evenings from 19th June to 28th August – 7.00pm to 9.00pm. Santa trains operate on 14th, 15th, 21st and 22nd December, 10.00am to 3.00pm. Please check the web site for details of Special Events.
Steam Working: Contact the Railway for details.
Prices: Adult Return £4.50   (Single £2.50)
          Child Return £2.00   (Single £1.50)
          Dogs 50p
Note: Joint fares are also available to include a Manx Electric Railway journey from Derby Castle.

Detailed Directions by Car:
The Railway is situated on the coast road to the north of Douglas.

HAMPTON & KEMPTON WATERWORKS RAILWAY

Address: Kempton Park Waterworks, Snakey Lane, Hanworth TW13 6XH	**Length of Line**: 315 yards at present
Telephone Nº: (01932) 765328	**Nº of Steam Locos**: 1
Year Formed: 2013	**Nº of Other Locos**: 3
Location of Line: Adjacent to the Kempton Steam Museum	**Approx Nº of Visitors P.A.**: 9,600
	Gauge: 2 feet
	Web: www.hamptonkemptonrailway.org.uk

GENERAL INFORMATION

Nearest Mainline Station: Kempton Park (¾ mile)
Nearest Bus Stop: Nailhead Road Roundabout (Bus service 290)
Car Parking: Available on site
Coach Parking: Available by arrangement
Souvenir Shop(s): In the Ticket Office
Food & Drinks: Available in the Kempton Great Engine House across the road.

SPECIAL INFORMATION

The line is located on the site of the Metropolitan Water Board's industrial railway which was first opened in 1915. Work has commenced on an extension of the line to Hampton.

OPERATING INFORMATION

Opening Times: 2019 dates: Every Sunday from 17th March to 17th November, open from 10.30am to 4.00pm. Special Event days are scheduled each month (see the web site for full details) including Ghost Nights on 1st & 2nd November and Santa Specials on 7th, 8th, 14th & 16th December (pre-booking required for both of these Special Events).
Steam Working: All operating days when possible.
Prices: Adults £3.00
Children £1.00 (Under-5s free of charge)

Detailed Directions by Car:
Near the North (London) end of the M3, the A316 is elevated. Look for the two chimneys of the Kempton Steam Museum. Exit the elevated section of the A316 (Country Way) down to the roundabout below the A316 and follow the brown tourist signs for the Kempton Steam Museum, with a garage on the right and the Müller Dairy on the left, turn left into Snakey Lane and left again into Kempton Waterworks Driveway. (SATNAV: TW13 7ND)

HASTINGS MINIATURE RAILWAY

Address: Rock-a-Nore Station, Old Town, Hastings   TN34 3DW
Telephone Nº: 07773 645228
Year Formed: 1948
Location: Between Hastings Old Town and the Historic Fishing Beach & Museum
Length of Line: 680 yards

Nº of Steam Locos: None
Nº of Other Locos: 8
Approx Nº of Visitors P.A.: 20,000
Gauge: 10¼ inches
Web: www.hastingsminiaturerailway.co.uk

GENERAL INFORMATION

Nearest Mainline Station: Hastings (1 mile)
Car Parking: Limited parking available nearby
Coach Parking: None
Souvenir Shop(s): Yes
Food & Drinks: Available nearby

SPECIAL INFORMATION

The Hastings Miniature Railway, which opened on 5th June 1948, runs along the sea front area of Hastings Old Town and is a popular attraction.

OPERATING INFORMATION

Opening Times: Weekends throughout the year from 11.00am to 5.00pm (12.00pm to 4.00pm during the winter months) and also daily during through the School Holidays and during the Autumn half-term holidays.

Steam Working: 'Edmund Hannay' runs on certain days throughout the year, fine weather permitting.

Prices: Adult Return £3.00
             Child Return £3.00
             Adult Day Rover £7.00
             Child Day Rover £5.50
             Family Day Rover £22.00
                       (2 Adults + 2 Children)

Detailed Directions by Car:
The Railway is located to the eastern (Fisherman's End) of Hastings Old Town, just off the A259 and next to the Hastings Fishing Museum.

HAYLING RAILWAY

Address: Eastoke, Sea Front Road, Hayling Island, Hampshire PO11 9HL	**N° of Steam Locos**: Visiting locos only
Telephone N°: 07775 696912	**N° of Other Locos**: 4
Year Formed: 2001	**N° of Members**: Approximately 100
Location: Eastoke to Beachlands	**Annual Membership Fee**: £15.00
Length of Line: 1 mile	**Approx N° of Visitors P.A.**: 25,000
Web site: www.haylingrailway.com	**Gauge**: 2 feet

GENERAL INFORMATION

Nearest Mainline Station: Havant
Nearest Bus Station: Beachlands
Car Parking: Spaces are available at both Beachlands and Eastoke Corner.
Coach Parking: Beachlands and Eastoke Corner
Souvenir Shop(s): Yes, at Eastoke
Food & Drinks: Available

SPECIAL INFORMATION

The Railway runs along Hayling Island beach front where there are fantastic views across the Solent to the Isle of Wight.

OPERATING INFORMATION

Opening Times: Every Saturday, Sunday and Wednesday throughout the year and daily during the local School holidays. Various specials run at different times of the year – please check the web site or phone the Railway for further details. The first train normally departs at 10.40am from Eastoke and 11.00am from Beachlands.

Steam Working: Visiting locos only. Please contact the railway for further information.

Prices: Adult Return £4.00
Child Return £3.00 (Under-3s ride free)
Senior Citizen Return £3.00
Family Return £9.00 (2 Adult + 2 Child)

Detailed Directions by Car:
Exit the A27 at Havant Roundabout and proceed along the A3023 towards Hayling Island seafront, following signs to Beachlands. Turn left at the funfair roundabout and follow the sefront road for 1 mile. Parking is available behind the Eastoke Station.

HEATHERSLAW LIGHT RAILWAY

Address: Ford Forge, Heatherslaw, Cornhill-on-Tweed TD12 4TJ	**Nº of Steam Locos**: 2
Telephone Nº: (01890) 820244	**Nº of Other Locos**: 2
Year Formed: 1989	**Approx Nº of Visitors P.A.**: 30,000
Location of Line: Ford & Etal Estates between Wooler & Berwick	**Gauge**: 15 inches
Length of Line: 2 miles	**Website**: www.heatherslawlightrailway.co.uk
	E-mail: info@heatherslawlightrailway.co.uk

GENERAL INFORMATION

Nearest Mainline Station: Berwick-upon-Tweed (10 miles)
Nearest Bus Station: Berwick-upon-Tweed (10 mls)
Car Parking: Available on site
Coach Parking: Available on site
Souvenir Shop(s): Yes
Food & Drinks: Available

SPECIAL INFORMATION

The railway runs from Heatherslaw to Etal Castle along the banks of the River Till. A choice of semi-open and fully enclosed coaches are available to passengers, even on the wettest of days!

OPERATING INFORMATION

Opening Times: 2019 dates: Daily from 24th March to 3rd November inclusive. Trains run hourly from 11.00am to 3.00pm (until 4.00pm in July & August)
Steam Working: Daily except when maintenance is being carried out on the engine.
Prices: Adult Return £7.50
        Child Return £4.50   (Under-5s: £3.00)
        Senior Citizen Return £6.50

Detailed Directions by Car:
From the North: Take the A697 from Coldstream and the railway is about 5 miles along.
From the South: Take the A697 from Wooler and Millfield.

ISLE OF MAN STEAM RAILWAY

Address: Isle of Man Railways, Banks Circus, Douglas, Isle of Man   IM1 5PT
Telephone Nº: (01624) 662525
Year Formed: 1873
Location of Line: Douglas to Port Erin
Length of Line: 15½ miles

Nº of Steam Locos: 16 (4 in service)
Nº of Other Locos: 2
Approx Nº of Visitors P.A.: 140,000
Gauge: 3 feet
Web site: www.rail.im

GENERAL INFORMATION

Nearest Mainline Station: Not applicable
Car Parking: Limited parking at all stations
Coach Parking: Available at Port Erin
Souvenir Shop(s): Souvenirs are available from all manned stations and from the shop at Port Erin Railway Museum
Food & Drinks: Yes – Douglas & Port Erin stations

SPECIAL INFORMATION

The Isle of Man Steam Railway is operated by the Isle of Man Government. A number of special events are held at the railway throughout the year.

OPERATING INFORMATION

Opening Times: 2019 dates: Daily from 8th March to 3rd November but closed on Tuesdays and Wednesdays in March and October. Also closed on 2nd & 3rd April and 1st & 2nd May. Day and evening services are available during some of the summer months. Please contact the railway or check the web site for further details.
Steam Working: All scheduled services
Prices: Prices vary with 1, 3, 5 & 7 day travel cards also available which include travel on buses, the Snaefell and Manx Electric Railways.

Detailed Directions:
By Sea from Heysham (Lancashire) or Liverpool to reach Isle of Man. By Air from Belfast, Birmingham, Dublin, Glasgow, Gloucester, Jersey, Liverpool, Manchester, Newcastle, Bristol and London. Douglas Station is ½ mile inland from the Sea Terminal at the end of North Quay.

KERR'S MINIATURE RAILWAY

Address: West Links Park, Arbroath, Tayside DD11 1QD	**N° of Other Locos**: 5
	Approx N° of Visitors P.A.: 5,000
Telephone N°: None	**Gauge**: 10¼ inches
Year Formed: 1935	**Website**: www.kerrsminiaturerailway.co.uk
Location: Seafront, West Links Park	**E-mail**: info@kerrsminiaturerailway.co.uk
Length of Line: 400 yards	
N° of Steam Locos: 2	

GENERAL INFORMATION

Nearest Mainline Station: Arbroath (1½ miles)
Nearest Bus Station: Arbroath (1½ miles)
Car Parking: Available 600 yards from railway
Coach Parking: Available 600 yards from railway
Souvenir Shop(s): Gifts available
Food & Drinks: Cafe stall in West Links Park

SPECIAL INFORMATION

The Railway is Scotland's oldest passenger-carrying miniature railway. It is a family-run enterprise not run for profit which is staffed by volunteers. The track itself runs alongside the Dundee to Aberdeen mainline. A miniature Bus and Fire Engine also operates, providing rides along the promenade for children.

OPERATING INFORMATION

Opening Times: 2019 dates: Open from April to September. Trains run at weekends and daily during the local school holidays in April, July and August. Opening times are 11.00am to 4.00pm, weather permitting.
Steam Working: Please contact the railway for further information.
Prices: Adults £2.00
　　　　　　Children £2.00

Detailed Directions by Car:
From All Parts: West Links Park is a seaside location which runs parallel to the A92 Coastal Tourist Route in Arbroath. Turn off the A92 at the West Links Park/KMR sign. The railway is then 600 yards due West along the seafront.

KIRKLEES LIGHT RAILWAY

Address: Park Mill Way, Clayton West, near Huddersfield, W. Yorks. HD8 9XJ	**N° of Steam Locos**: 6
Telephone N°: (01484) 865727	**N° of Other Locos**: 2
Year Formed: 1991	**Approx N° of Visitors P.A.**: 57,000
Location of Line: Clayton West to Shelley	**Gauge**: 15 inches
Length of Line: 3½ miles	**Web site**: www.kirkleeslightrailway.com
	E-mail: info@kirkleeslightrailway.com

GENERAL INFORMATION

Nearest Mainline Station: Denby Dale (4 miles)
Nearest Bus Station: Bus stops at the bottom of Park Mill Way. Take the 435 and 436 from Wakefield or the 80 and 81 from Huddersfield.
Car Parking: Ample free parking at site
Coach Parking: Ample free parking at site
Souvenir Shop(s): Yes
Food & Drinks: Yes

SPECIAL INFORMATION

The Railway has outdoor play areas for children, a 7¼ inch railway at Clayton West and a café and tearooms which are open during railway operations.

OPERATING INFORMATION

Opening Times: 2019 dates: Every weekend and Bank Holiday from mid-February to the end of December and daily during school holidays. Open Wednesday to Sunday from 5th June to 21st July and daily from 22nd July to 1st September.
Steam Working: All trains are steam-hauled (subject to availability). Train timetables vary, so please check the website for further information.
Prices: Adults £7.50
  Children (3-16 years) £5.50
  Children (under 3 years) Free of charge
  Concessions £6.50
  Family Ticket £24.00
Note: Prices at Special events may vary.

Detailed Directions by Car:
The Railway is located on the A636 Wakefield to Denby Dale road. Turn off the M1 at Junction 39 and follow the A636 signposted for Denby Dale. Continue for approximately 4 miles then the railway is on the left after passing under the railway bridge and is situated at the top of the Industrial Estate, just before the village of Scissett.

LAKESHORE RAILROAD

Address: South Marine Park, South Shields NE33 2NN	**Nº of Steam Locos:** 2
Correspondence: 6 Marina Drive, South Shields NE33 2NH	**Nº of Other Locos:** 1
	Approx Nº of Visitors P.A.: 65,000
Telephone Nº: 07745 350983	**Gauge:** 9½ inches
Year Formed: 1972	**Web site:** www.lakeshorerailroad.co.uk
Length of Line: 570 yards	**E-mail:** info@lakeshorerailroad.co.uk

GENERAL INFORMATION

Nearest Mainline Station: South Shields (¾ mile)
Nearest Bus Station: South Shields (1 mile)
Car Parking: Available on the seafront
Coach Parking: Available nearby
Souvenir Shop(s): None
Food & Drinks: Available nearby

SPECIAL INFORMATION

The Lakeshore Railroad runs two American-designed locomotives – hence the name!

OPERATING INFORMATION

Opening Times: Weekends throughout the year and daily from mid-May to mid-September and during other School Holidays except for Christmas. Trains run from 11.00am to 5.00pm (until 6.00pm during the summer months).
Steam Working: Daily, subject to availability
Prices: Adults £1.50
   Children £1.50 (Free for Under-3s)

Detailed Directions by Car:
From All Parts: Take the A194 into South Shields. The railway is located by the Seafront in South Marine Park and can be found by following the brown tourist signs marked for the 'Seafront'.

LANCASHIRE MINING MUSEUM

Address: Higher Green Lane, Astley, Manchester M29 7JB	**N° of Steam Locos:** None
Telephone N°: (01942) 895841	**N° of Other Locos:** 33
Year Formed: 1983	**N° of Members:** 120
Location of Line: Astley Green Colliery	**Approx N° of Visitors P.A.:** 6,000
Length of Line: 440 yards	**Gauge:** 2 feet
	Web site: lancashireminingmuseum.org

GENERAL INFORMATION

Nearest Mainline Station: Salford (3 miles)
Nearest Bus Station: Leigh (3 miles)
Car Parking: Available on site
Coach Parking: Available
Food & Drinks: Snack and hot drinks available. Also open for special Afternoon Tea events during the year. Check the Museum web site for details.

SPECIAL INFORMATION

The Lancashire Mining Museum houses the largest collection of underground colliery locos in the UK. The 440 yard line is used for freight demonstrations.

OPERATING INFORMATION

Opening Times: Tuesday, Thursday and weekends throughout the year except for Christmas Day and Boxing Day. Also open at other times by prior arrangement. Open from 1.30pm to 5.00pm.
Steam Working: None
Prices: No admission charge but donations are gratefully accepted.
Note: Although the museum does not offer passenger rides at present, it is currently upgrading the railway infrastructure and two locomotives with the intention of offering rides in the future.

Detailed Directions by Car:
From All Parts: Exit the M6 at Junction 23 and take the A580 towards Manchester. After about 6 miles cross the Bridgewater Canal then take the next right signposted Higher Green. After approximately ¼ mile turn left into the Colliery grounds.

LAPPA VALLEY STEAM RAILWAY

Address: St. Newlyn East, Newquay, Cornwall TR8 5LX
Telephone Nº: (01872) 510317
Year Formed: 1974
Location of Line: Benny Halt to East Wheal Rose, near St. Newlyn East
Length of Line: 1¼ miles

Nº of Steam Locos: 4
Nº of Other Locos: 2
Approx Nº of Visitors P.A.: 70,000
Gauge: 15 inches
Web site: www.lappavalley.co.uk

GENERAL INFORMATION

Nearest Mainline Station: Newquay (5 miles)
Nearest Bus Station: Newquay (5 miles)
Car Parking: Free parking at Benny Halt
Coach Parking: Free parking is available at Benny Halt
Souvenir Shop(s): Yes
Food & Drinks: Yes

SPECIAL INFORMATION

The railway runs on part of the former Newquay to Chacewater branch line. Site also has a Grade II listed mine building, boating, play areas for children and 2 other miniature train rides.

OPERATING INFORMATION

Opening Times: 2019 dates: Daily from 30th March to 3rd November.
Steam Working: 10.40am to 4.00pm during the summer months.
Prices: Adult £12.95
Child £10.95
Family £43.00
(2 adults + 2 children)
Family £46.00
(2 adults + 3 children)
Senior Citizen £10.95

Detailed Directions by Car:
The railway is signposted from the A30 at the Summercourt-Mitchell bypass, from the A3075 south of Newquay and the A3058 east of Newquay.

LAUNCESTON STEAM RAILWAY

Address: The Old Gasworks, St. Thomas Road, Launceston, Cornwall   PL15 8DA
Telephone Nº: (01566) 775665
Year Formed: Opened in 1983
Location of Line: Launceston to Newmills
Length of Line: 2½ miles

Nº of Steam Locos: 3
Nº of Other Locos: 4
Gauge: 1 foot 11 $^5/_8$ inches
Web site: www.launcestonsr.co.uk

GENERAL INFORMATION

Nearest Mainline Station: Liskeard (15 miles)
Nearest Bus Station: Launceston (½ mile)
Car Parking: At the Station, Newport Industrial Estate, Launceston
Coach Parking: As above
Souvenir Shop(s): Yes – also with a bookshop
Food & Drinks: Cafe serving hot and cold meals

SPECIAL INFORMATION

The Launceston Steam Railway runs for two and a half miles through the glorious Kensey Valley along the trackbed of the old North Cornwall Railway, where once express trains from Waterloo passed.

OPERATING INFORMATION

Opening Times: 2019 dates: 14th to 19th and 21st to 26th April; 19th to 24th and 26th to 31st May; Sunday to Thursday from 2nd June to 11th July and 1st to 26th September then daily (though closed on Saturdays) from 14th July to 30th August. Also open daily from 20th to 25th October and 27th October to 1st November.
Steam Working: Hourly from 11.00am to 4.00pm.
Prices: Adult Return £11.25
          Child Return £7.25
          Family Return £31.25 (2 adult + 4 child)
          Senior Citizen Return £9.50
Group rates are available upon application.

Detailed Directions by Car:
From the East/West: Drive to Launceston via the A30 and look for the brown Steam Engine Tourist signs. Use the L.S.R. car park at the Newport Industrial Estate; From Bude/Holsworthy: Take the A388 to Launceston and follow signs for the town centre. After the river bridge turn left at the traffic lights into Newport Industrial Estate and use the L.S.R. car park. Sat Navs use the following post code: PL15 8EX.

LEADHILLS & WANLOCKHEAD RAILWAY

Address: The Station, Leadhills, Lanarkshire   ML12 6XP
Telephone Nº: None
Year Formed: 1983
Location of Line: Leadhills, Lanarkshire
Length of Line: ¾ mile (at present)

Nº of Steam Locos: 2 + a visiting loco
Nº of Other Locos: 7
Nº of Members: Approximately 100
Annual Membership Fee: Adult £15.00
Approx Nº of Visitors P.A.: 3,000
Gauge: 2 feet
Web site: www.leadhillsrailway.co.uk

GENERAL INFORMATION

Nearest Mainline Station: Sanquhar
Nearest Bus Station: Lanark and Sanquhar
Car Parking: Available on site
Coach Parking: Available on site
Souvenir Shop(s): Yes
Food & Drinks: Yes

SPECIAL INFORMATION

Leadhills & Wanlockhead Railway is the highest adhesion railway in the UK with the summit 1,498 feet above sea level.

OPERATING INFORMATION

Opening Times: Weekends from Easter until the end of September. There are also a number of 'Special Events' during the year. Please contact the railway for further information about these. Trains run from 10.45am to 4.00pm on operating days.
Steam Working: Please check the website for details.
Prices: Adult Day Ticket £5.00
          Child Day Ticket £2.50
          Family Day Ticket £12.00
              (2 adults and up to 2 children)

Detailed Directions by Car:
From the South: Exit the M74 at Junction 14 and follow the A702 to Elvanfoot. Turn right onto the B7040 and follow to Leadhills. Turn left at the T-junction and Station Road is a short distance on the left; From the North: Exit the M74 at Junction 13 for Abington and follow signs for Leadhills along the B797. Station Road is on the left shortly after entering Leadhills.

LEIGHTON BUZZARD RAILWAY

Address: Pages Park Station, Billington Road, Leighton Buzzard, Beds. LU7 4TN
Telephone N°: (01525) 373888
E-mail: info@buzzrail.co.uk
Year Formed: 1967
Location of Line: Leighton Buzzard
Length of Line: 3 miles

N° of Steam Locos: 14
N° of Other Locos: 53
N° of Members: 400
Annual Membership Fee: £25.00
Approx N° of Visitors P.A.: 20,000
Gauge: 2 feet
Web site: www.buzzrail.co.uk

GENERAL INFORMATION

Nearest Mainline Station: Leighton Buzzard (2 miles)
Nearest Bus Station: Leighton Buzzard (¾ mile)
Car Parking: Free parking adjacent
Coach Parking: Free parking adjacent
Souvenir Shop(s): Yes   **Food & Drinks:** Yes

SPECIAL INFORMATION

The railway was constructed in 1919 to carry sand from local quarries using surplus materials from World War I battlefield supply lines. Now a working museum, it transports passengers and is operated by volunteers.

OPERATING INFORMATION

Opening Times: 2019 dates: Sundays from 24th March to 27th October plus Bank Holiday weekends. Also open on some Saturdays and weekdays. Trains run from 10.30am to 4.00pm and a return journey takes 80 minutes. Christmas and New Year services run on some dates in December. Please visit the railway's web site for further details.
Steam Working: Most operating days.
Prices: Adult £10.50
      Child £6.50   (Under-2s ride for free)
      Senior Citizens £9.00
Note: A variety of Family Tickets, Day Rover tickets and Single tickets are also available. The prices shown above include an optional Gift Aid donation.

Detailed Directions by Car:
Travel to Leighton Buzzard then follow the brown tourist signs showing a steam train. Pages Park Station is ¾ mile to the south of the Town Centre. From the A505/A4146 bypass, turn towards Leighton Buzzard at the roundabout following the 'Narrow Gauge Railway' brown tourist signs.

LINCOLNSHIRE COAST LIGHT RAILWAY

Address: Skegness Water Leisure Park, Walls Lane, Skegness   PE25 1JF
Telephone Nº: (01754) 897400
E-mail: john@chappellandcosurveyors.co.uk
Year Formed: 1960 (re-opened in 2009)
Location of Line: Skegness
Length of Line: ¾ miles

Nº of Steam Locos: 1
Nº of Other Locos: 6
Nº of Members: Approximately 50
Approx Nº of Visitors P.A.: 5,000
Gauge: 2 feet
Web site: www.lclr.co.uk

GENERAL INFORMATION

Nearest Mainline Station: Skegness (3 miles)
Nearest Bus Station: Butlins (½ miles)
Car Parking: Free parking available on site
Coach Parking: Free parking available on site
Souvenir Shop(s): None
Food & Drinks: Available

SPECIAL INFORMATION

The railway re-opened in 2009, after relocating from its' original home in Humberston, where it ran from 1960 to 1985. It is home to a unique collection of English narrow gauge railway carriages, vehicles and locomotives, many of which saw service in the trench warfare during the First World War.

OPERATING INFORMATION

Opening Times: 2019 dates: 15th June; 13th, 20th, 27th and 31st July; 3rd, 7th, 10th, 14th, 17th, 21st, 24th, 25th, 28th and 31st August; 15th September. Further dates may be added to the timetable during the year. Please check the web site for details of these.
Trains run between 11.00am and 3.45pm.
Steam Working: The newly-restored Peckett 0-6-0 locomotive "Jurassic" is now in steam and will operate services on the afternoons of 13th, 20th & 27th July; 3rd, 10th, 17th, 24th, 25th & 31st August and the 15th September.
Prices: Adults £1.00
            Children £1.00

Detailed Directions by Car:
From All Parts: Take the A52 North from Skegness (signposted for Ingoldmells) and continue for 3 miles. Turn left onto Walls Lane opposite the Butlins signposted for the Water Leisure Park. After ¼ mile turn left into the Park and follow the signs for the Railway.

LITTLEHAMPTON RAILWAY

Address: Mewsbrook Park, Hendon Avenue, Littlehampton BN16 2LX	**Nº of Steam Locos**: None
Telephone Nº: 07436 562933	**Nº of Other Locos**: 3
Information Nº: 07746 907817	**Nº of Members**: Approximately 50
Year Formed: 1948	**Approx Nº of Visitors P.A.**: 18,000
Location of Line: Mewsbrook Park	**Gauge**: 12¼ inches
Length of Line: ½ mile	**Web**: www.littlehamptonminiaturerailway.com
	E-mail: littlehamptonminiaturerailway@gmail.com

GENERAL INFORMATION

Nearest Mainline Station: Littlehampton (1 mile)
Nearest Bus Station: Littlehampton
Car Parking: Available at the swimming pool, at East Green and along the Sea Wall.
Coach Parking: Available at the swimming pool
Souvenir Shop(s): During special event days only
Food & Drinks: Cafes are adjacent to both stations

SPECIAL INFORMATION

The Littlehampton Railway is the oldest 12¼ inch gauge railway in the UK and runs from Mewsbrook Park to Norfolk Gardens. The railway is surrounded by a variety of leisure attractions including a boating lake and a 9-hole golf course.

OPERATING INFORMATION

Opening Times: Weekends and School Holidays from 6th April to 3rd November (weather permitting). Trains run daily from 11.00am then every 30 minutes until 4.00pm. Santa Specials also operate on 14th and 15th December.
Steam Working: None at present
Prices: Adult Return £3.00
Child Return £2.00 (Under-3s free)
Family Ticket Return £9.00
(2 adults + 2 children)

Detailed Directions by Car:
From All Parts: Take the A27 Brighton to Portsmouth road and follow signs for Littlehampton. Upon entering Littlehampton, follow signs for the Swimming Pool/Sea Front and, when you reach the Beach Road (which runs along parallel to the sea), head east and park either at East Green or further along to the Swimming Pool.

LLANBERIS LAKE RAILWAY

Address: Gilfach Ddu, Llanberis, Gwynedd   LL55 4TY
Telephone Nº: (01286) 870549
Year Formed: 1970
Location of Line: Just off the A4086 Caernarfon to Capel Curig road at Llanberis
Length of Line: 2½ miles

Nº of Steam Locos: 3
Nº of Other Locos: 2
Approx Nº of Visitors P.A.: 80,000
Gauge: 1 foot 11½ inches
Web site: www.lake-railway.co.uk
E-mail: sales@lake-railway.co.uk

GENERAL INFORMATION

Nearest Mainline Station: Bangor (8 miles)
Nearest Bus Station: Caernarfon (6 miles) (there is a bus stop by Llanberis Station)
Car Parking: £4.00 Council car park on site
Coach Parking: Ample free parking on site
Souvenir Shop(s): Yes
Food & Drinks: Yes

SPECIAL INFORMATION

Llanberis Lake Railway runs along part of the trackbed of the Padarn Railway which transported slates for export and closed in 1961.

OPERATING INFORMATION

Opening Times: 2019 dates: Open most days from 24th March to 31st October, excluding some Saturdays in April, May and September and some Fridays and Saturdays in October. Open Tuesdays to Thursdays only in November and on some dates in December. Please send for a free timetable or check out the railway's web site where an online booking feature is also available.
Steam Working: Every operating day.
Trains generally run from 11.00am to 4.00pm.
Prices: Adult £9.00   Child £4.50
                 Concessions £8.00
Family tickets are £24.00 (2 adults + 2 children) and a range of other discounts are available.
Note: The Welsh Slate Museum is situated adjacent to the Railway.

Detailed Directions by Car:
The railway is situated just off the A4086 Caernarfon to Capel Curig road. Follow signs for Padarn Country Park.

LOCOMOTION

Address: Locomotion, Dale Road, Shildon   DL4 2RE
Telephone Nº: (01904) 685780
Year Formed: 2004
Location: Shildon, County Durham
Length of Line: Over ½ mile

Nº of Steam Locos: 70+ locomotives and other rail vehicles
Approx Nº of Visitors P.A.: 200,000
Gauge: Standard
Web site: www.locomotion.org.uk

GENERAL INFORMATION

Nearest Mainline Station: Shildon (adjacent)
Nearest Bus Station: Durham
Car Parking: Available on site
Coach Parking: Available on site
Souvenir Shop(s): Yes
Food & Drinks: Yes

SPECIAL INFORMATION

A Locomotion you can see highlights of the British National Collection of railway vehicles in the world's first railway town. The museum is home to more than 70 National Rail Collection vehicles, including such icons as 'Sans Pareil', 'APT-E' and the Deltic prototype.

OPERATING INFORMATION

Opening Times: 2019 dates: Open daily but closed from 24th to 26th December and on 1st January. During the winter months (November to March), the Museum is open from 10.00am to 4.00pm. The whole site is open daily during the summer (1st April to 31st October) – 10.00am to 5.00pm.
Steam Working: On special event days – contact the museum or check the web site for further details.
Prices: Admission to the Museum is free of charge.
Train Rides: Adults £3.00
                Concessions £2.00

Detailed Directions by Car:
From All Parts: Exit the A1(M) at Junction 58 and take the A68 and the A6072 to Shildon. Follow the Brown tourist signs to Locomotion which is situated ¼ mile to the south-east of the Town Centre.
Drivers using SATNAVs should enter the following post code: DL4 2RE

LONDON MUSEUM OF WATER & STEAM

Address: London Museum of Water & Steam, Green Dragon Lane, Brentford, TW8 0EN **Telephone N°**: (020) 8568-4757 **Year Formed**: 1986 **Location of Line**: Greater London **Length of Line**: Under 1 mile	**N° of Steam Locos**: 1 **Other Locos**: 1 **N° of Members**: 750 **Annual Membership Fee**: £25.00 (Adult) **Approx N° of Visitors P.A.**: 20,000 **Gauge**: 2 feet **Web site**: www.waterandsteam.org.uk **E-mail**: museum@waterandsteam.org.uk

GENERAL INFORMATION

Nearest Mainline Station: Kew Bridge (3 minute walk)
Nearest Bus Station: Bus stop across the road – Services 65, 267 and 237
Car Parking: Spaces for 20 cars available on site
Coach Parking: Available on site – book in advance
Souvenir Shop(s): Yes
Food & Drinks: Cafe open 11.00am to 4.00pm

SPECIAL INFORMATION

The Museum is a former Victorian Pumping Station with a collection of working Steam Pumping Engines. The Railway demonstrates typical water board use of Railways.

OPERATING INFO

Opening Times: The museum is open 10.00am to 4.00pm Wednesday to Sunday inclusive and daily during the local school holidays. Please check the website for further information before visiting.
Steam Working: The pumping engines are in steam every weekend throughout the year and the railway is in steam every weekend from 1st April to New Year.
Prices: Adults From £12.50
        Under-16s From £5.50
                (Under-5s free of charge)
        Senior Citizen From £11.00
        Family Ticket From £30.50
                (2 adults + 2 children)
        Family Ticket From £18.00
                (1 adult + 2 children)
Note: Annual tickets cost just £4.00 more than the daily prices shown!

Detailed Directions by Car:
From All Parts: Exit the M4 at Junction 1 and follow the A4 to Chiswick Roundabout. Take the exit signposted for Kew Gardens & Brentford. Go straight on at the next two sets of traffic lights following A315 towards Brentford. After 2nd set of lights take the first right for the Museum. The Museum is next to the tall Victorian tower.

LYNTON & BARNSTAPLE RAILWAY

Address: Woody Bay Station, Martinhoe Cross, Parracombe, Devon EX31 4RA **Telephone Nº**: (01598) 763487 **E-mail**: enquiries@lynton-rail.co.uk **Year Formed**: 1993 **Location of Line**: North Devon **Length of Line**: One mile	**Nº of Steam Locos**: 3 **Nº of Other Locos**: 3 **Nº of Members**: 2,500 **Annual Membership Fee**: £30.00 **Approx Nº of Visitors P.A.**: 50,000 **Gauge**: 1 foot 11½ inches **Web site**: www.lynton-rail.co.uk

Photo courtesy of Trevor A. Garnham

GENERAL INFORMATION

Nearest Mainline Station: Barnstaple
Nearest Bus Station: Barnstaple
Car Parking: Available at Woody Bay Station
Coach Parking: Available by prior arrangement
Souvenir Shop(s): Yes – at Woody Bay Station
Food & Drinks: Available at Woody Bay Station

SPECIAL INFORMATION

Original Lynton & Barnstaple Railway carriages built in 1898 and 1903 are now operating a regular passenger service. At present, trains are only running between Woody Bay Station and Killington Lane Halt due to reconstruction work.

OPERATING INFORMATION

Opening Times: Open most days from late March to early November and selected dates in December. Please check with the railway for exact dates. Trains run from 10.45am to 4.00pm.
Steam Working: All trains are steam-hauled except on Mondays and Fridays outside of the school holidays or in the event of breakdown.
Prices: Adult Return £7.50
Child Return £3.00 (Ages 5-14)
Senior Citizen Return £6.50
Family Ticket £18 (2 Adults + 3 Children)
Note: Upgrades to First Class are available for £3.00 per person.

Detailed Directions by Car:
From All Parts: Woody Bay Station is located alongside the A39 halfway between Lynton and Blackmoor Gate and one mile north-east of the village of Parracombe.

MARGAM PARK RAILWAY

Address: Margam Country Park, Port Talbot SA13 2TJ	**Nº of Steam Locos**: None
	Nº of Other Locos: 1
Telephone Nº: (01639) 881635	**Approx Nº of Visitors P.A.**: 200,000 (to
Year Formed: 1976	the Park itself, not just the railway!)
Location of Line: Margam Country Park	**Gauge**: 2 feet
Length of Line: Almost 1½ miles	**Web site**: www.margamcountrypark.co.uk

GENERAL INFORMATION

Nearest Mainline Station: Port Talbot (3 miles)
Nearest Bus Station: Port Talbot (3 miles)
Car Parking: Available on site for a £6.00 charge
Coach Parking: Available
Souvenir Shop(s): Yes
Food & Drinks: Available

SPECIAL INFORMATION

Set in 1,000 acres of glorious parkland, Margam Country Park features an 18th Century Orangery, a Tudor-Gothic Victorian Mansion House and a 12th Century Chapter House.

OPERATING INFORMATION

Opening Times: 2019 dates: The railway operates at weekends, bank holidays and daily throughout the school holidays during the spring and summer seasons. The railway is closed during the autumn and winter months. Please check the web site for further information.
Steam Working: None at present
Prices: Adults £2.40
Children £1.20 (Under-3s ride for free)
Concessions £1.20
Family Ticket £6.60 (2 adults + 2 children)
Note: Entrance to Margam Park is usually free, but there may be admission charges on special event days (usually Bank Holidays). Please check the web site for further details.

Detailed Directions by Car:
From All Parts: Exit the M4 at Junction 38 and take the A48 towards Pyle following the brown tourist signs for Margam Country Park. The Park is situated on the left hand side of the road.

MOSELEY INDUSTRIAL NARROW GAUGE TRAMWAY, TOY AND MINING MUSEUM

Address: Tumblydown Farm,
Tolgus Mount, Redruth   TR15 3TA
Telephone Nº: (01209) 211191
Alternative Telephone Nº: 07511 256677
Year Formed: 1969 (formed in the
northwest, relocated to Cornwall in 2000)
Location: ½ mile north of Redruth

Length of Line: 800 yards
Nº of Steam Locos: 1 road locomotive
Nº of Other Locos: 20
Approx Nº of Visitors P.A.: 7,000
Gauge: 2 feet
Web site: www.tumblydownfarm.co.uk

GENERAL INFORMATION

Nearest Mainline Station: Redruth (2 miles)
Nearest Bus Station: Redruth (2 miles)
Car Parking: Available on site
Coach Parking: Available by prior arrangement
Souvenir Shop(s): Yes
Food & Drinks: Available by prior arrangement

SPECIAL INFORMATION

Moseley Museum is operated by volunteers who
maintain and restore the vehicles and displays.
Other attractions at the museum include collections
of vintage toys and meccano, curios and mining
equipment. Home of the Murdoch Flyer.

OPERATING INFORMATION

Opening Times: Open throughout the year for
group and individual visits by prior arrangement,
plus a number of special public open days. Also
open on all Monday and Thursday afternoons.
Please contact the museum for further details before
visiting.
Steam Working: Operational road locomotive, 'The
Murdoch Flyer'.
Prices: Free of charge but voluntary donations are
gratefully received!

Detailed Directions by Car:
From the A30, turn on to the old Redruth bypass (A3047). Follow the brown tourist signs for Trickys Lodge.
Tumblydown Farm is on the right about 200 yards past Tricky's Lodge.

NATIONAL RAILWAY MUSEUM – YORK

Address: National Railway Museum,
Leeman Road, York   YO26 4XJ
Telephone Nº: 03330 161010
Year Formed: 1975
Location of Line: York
Length of Line: Short demonstration line

Nº of Steam Locos: 79
Nº of Other Locos: 37
Approx Nº of Visitors P.A.: 900,000
Web site: www.nrm.org.uk
E-mail: info@railwaymuseum.org.uk

GENERAL INFORMATION

Nearest Mainline Station: York (¼ mile)
Nearest Bus Station: York (¼ mile)
Car Parking: On site long stay car park
Coach Parking: On site
Souvenir Shop(s): Yes
Food & Drinks: Excellent on-site catering facilities.

SPECIAL INFORMATION

The Museum is the greatest of its kind in the world,
housing the Nation's collection of locomotives,
carriages, uniforms, posters and an extensive
photographic archive. Special events and exhibitions
run throughout the year. A 7¼ inch miniature
railway offers rides in the South Yard area.

OPERATING INFORMATION

Opening Times: Open daily 10.00am to 6.00pm (or
5.00pm during the winter months). Closed from
24th to 26th of December.
Steam Working: School holidays – please phone to
confirm details
Prices: Free admission but visitors are invited to
make a donation. (Excludes some Special events
and Steam rides). Phone 08448 153139 for details.

Detailed Directions by Car:
The Museum is located in the centre of York, just behind the Railway Station. It is clearly signposted from all
approaches to York.

NORTH BAY MINIATURE RAILWAY

Address: Burniston Road, Scarborough, North Yorkshire YO12 6PF
Telephone Nº: (01723) 368791
Year Opened: 1931
Location: Peasholm Park to Scalby Mills
Length of Line: 1 mile

Nº of Steam Locos: 1
Nº of Other Locos: 4
Nº of Members: None
Approx Nº of Visitors P.A.: 200,000
Gauge: 20 inches
Web site: www.nbr.org.uk
E-mail: gm@nbr.org.uk

GENERAL INFORMATION

Nearest Mainline Station:
Scarborough
Nearest Bus Station: Scarborough
Car Parking: Adjacent to the railway
Coach Parking:
Adjacent to the railway
Souvenir Shop(s): Yes
Food & Drinks: Drinks and snacks are available from the gift shop and Boatmans Tavern & Scampi Shack is open from May to September. Please check the web site for opening times.

SPECIAL INFORMATION

The North Bay Miniature Railway was opened in 1931 and operates between Northstead Manor and Scalby Mills for the Sea Life Centre.

OPERATING INFO

Opening Times: 2019 dates: Daily from 30th March until 3rd November and Santa Specials run on December weekends before Christmas. Services then operate at weekends from 14th February to 27th March 2020 and during the local school holidays. Trains run at varying times from 10.30am onwards, depending on the time of the year. Please phone (01723) 368791 or check the web site for further details.
Steam Working: Please check the web site for details.
Prices: Adult Return £4.00
(Single £3.00)
Child Return £3.00 (Age 3-15)
(Single £2.50)
Note: Season tickets are also available.

Detailed Directions by Car:
From All Parts: Take the A64, A165 or A170 to Scarborough and follow the signs for North Bay Leisure Park. The railway is situated just off the A165 opposite Peasholm Park. Alternatively, follow signs for the Sea Life Centre for Scalby Mills Station.

OLD KILN LIGHT RAILWAY

Address: Rural Life Centre, Reeds Road, Tilford, Farnham, Surrey GU10 2DL	**N° of Steam Locos**: 3 **Other Locos**: 8
Telephone N°: (01252) 795571	**N° of Members**: 14
Year Formed: 1975	**Annual Membership Fee**: £25.00
Location: 3 miles south of Farnham	**Approx N° of Visitors P.A.**: 21,000
Length of Line: ¾ mile	**Gauge**: 2 feet
	Web site: oldkilnlightrailway.co.uk

GENERAL INFORMATION

Nearest Mainline Station: Farnham (4 miles)
Nearest Bus Station: Farnham
Car Parking: Free parking available on site
Coach Parking: Free parking available on site
Souvenir Shop(s): Yes
Food & Drinks: Available

SPECIAL INFORMATION

The Railway is part of the Rural Life Centre at Tilford. The Centre contains the biggest country life collection in the South of England with a wide range of attractions. A line extension to ¾ mile has recently been opened.

OPERATING INFORMATION

Opening Times: The Centre is open Wednesday to Sunday and Bank Holidays, March to November, 10.00am to 5.00pm. Open Wednesdays and Sundays only during the winter from 11.00am to 4.00pm. Also open for Santa Specials in December. Train rides are available most Sundays and Bank Holidays. Please contact the railway for further details.
Steam Working: During Special Events only. Please check the web site for details.
Prices: Adult £11.00   Child £8.00 (Under-4s free)
　　　　Senior Citizen £10.00
　　　　Family Ticket 31.50 (2 adult + 3 child)
Note: Prices shown are for entry to the Rural Life Centre. During the winter prices are half those shown. Train rides are an additional charge of £2.00.

Detailed Directions by Car:
The Rural Life Centre is situated 3 miles south of Farnham. From Farnham take the A287 southwards before turning left at Millbridge crossroads into Reeds Road. The Centre is on the left after about ½ mile, just after the Frensham Garden Centre; From the A3: Turn off at the Hindhead crossroads and head north to Tilford. Pass through Tilford, cross the River Wey then turn left into Reeds Road. The Centre is on the right after ½ mile.

PERRYGROVE RAILWAY

Address: Perrygrove Railway, Coleford, Gloucestershire GL16 8QB	**No of Steam Locos**: 3
Telephone No: (01594) 834991	**No of Other Locos**: 3
Year Formed: 1996	**No of Members**: 20
Location of Line: ½ mile south of Coleford	**Approx No of Visitors P.A.**: 30,000
Length of Line: ¾ mile	**Gauge**: 15 inches
	Web site: www.perrygrove.co.uk

GENERAL INFORMATION

Nearest Mainline Station: Lydney (for Parkend)
Nearest Bus Station: Bus stops in Coleford
Car Parking: Free parking available on site
Coach Parking: Free parking on site
Souvenir Shop(s): Yes
Food & Drinks: Sandwiches & light refreshments are available

SPECIAL INFORMATION

Perrygrove is a unique railway with 4 stations, all with access to private woodland walks. Lots of picnic tables are available in the open and under cover. There is also an indoor village with secret passages, a play area and an exciting Treetop Adventure accessible to all.

OPERATING INFORMATION

Opening Times: Open every weekend, Tuesday and Thursday throughout the year and daily during the local school holidays. A number of Special Events are also held throughout the year including Santa Specials on weekends in December (pre-booking is essential for these). Please contact the railway for details. Opening hours vary depending on the season so please check the web site for details of the times before visiting.
Steam Working: Some services are steam-hauled, depending on the time of the year and driver experience courses are also available.
Prices: Adults: £7.35
Children: £5.95 (Under-3s ride free)
Senior Citizens: £6.95
Family Ticket: £25.75
(2 adults + 2 children)

Detailed Directions by Car:
From All Parts: Travel to Coleford, Gloucestershire. Upon reaching the vicinity of Coleford, the Perrygrove Railway is clearly signposted with brown tourist signs from all directions. SATNAVs use this post code: GL16 8QB

RAVENGLASS & ESKDALE RAILWAY

Address: Ravenglass, Cumbria CA18 1SW	**Gauge:** 15 inches
Telephone Nº: (01229) 717171	**Nº of Steam Locos:** 7 **Other Locos:** 8
Year Formed: 1875	**Nº of Members:** None
Location: The Lake District National Park	**Approx Nº of Visitors P.A.:** 120,000
Length of Line: 7 miles	**Web site:** www.ravenglass-railway.co.uk
	E-mail: steam@ravenglass-railway.co.uk

GENERAL INFORMATION

Nearest Mainline Station: Ravenglass (adjacent)
Nearest Bus Stop: Ravenglass
Car Parking: Available at both terminals
Coach Parking: At Ravenglass
Souvenir Shop(s): Yes   **Food & Drinks:** Yes

SPECIAL INFORMATION

The Ravenglass & Eskdale Railway is one of the oldest and longest narrow gauge railways in England, known affectionately as 'La'al Ratty', meaning "little railway" in the old Cumbrian dialect. The heritage steam engines transport passengers from Ravenglass, the only coastal village in the Lake District, through seven miles of spectacular scenery within sight of England's highest mountains, the Scafell Range, through to Dalegarth for Boot, some 210ft above sea level.

OPERATING INFORMATION

Opening Times: 2019 dates: The service runs daily from 16th March until 3rd November inclusive. Trains also run daily during February half-term and Christmas School Holidays and Santa Specials operate on weekends and other dates in December. Open from 9.00am to 5.00pm (sometimes later during high season).
Steam Working: Most services are steam hauled.
Prices: Adult £10.00 to £15.50
Child £6.00 to £9.30 (Ages 5 to 15)
Under-5s travel free
Family Ticket £27.50 to £44.95
(Unlimited travel for 2 adults + 2 children)
Note: Prices vary depending on the timetable in use, First Class upgrades are available and discounts are available for online purchases.

Detailed Directions by Car:
The railway is situated just off the main A595 Western Lake District road.

RHIW VALLEY LIGHT RAILWAY

Address: Lower House Farm, Manafon, Nr. Welshpool SY21 8BJ	**Nº of Steam Locos**: 2
Telephone Nº: None	**Nº of Other Locos**: 1
Year Formed: 1971	**Approx Nº of Visitors P.A.**: 1,000
Location of Line: By the side of the B4390 between Berriew and Manafon	**Annual Membership Fee**: £20.00
	Gauge: 15 inches
Length of Line: ¾ mile	**Web site**: www.rvlr.co.uk
	E-mail: steam@rvlr.co.uk

GENERAL INFORMATION

Nearest Mainline Station: Welshpool (5 miles)
Nearest Bus Station: Welshpool (5 miles)
Car Parking: Available on site
Coach Parking: Available on site
Souvenir Shop(s): None
Food & Drinks: Tea and coffee served during opening times.

SPECIAL INFORMATION

The Rhiw Valley Light Railway is planning projects to both extend the track and also construct a new waiting room.

OPERATING INFORMATION

Opening Times: 2019 operating dates:
4th & 5th May; 1st & 2nd June; 6th & 7th July; 3rd & 4th August; 7th & 8th September; 5th & 6th October. Gates open at 10.30am and trains run from 11.00pm to 4.30pm on each of these days.
Steam Working: During all operating days.
Prices: Adult £6.00
　　　　　　 Child £4.00 (Under-3s ride free)
　　　　　　 Family Tickets £20.00
　　　　　　　　　 (2 adults + 4 children)

Detailed Directions by Car:
Take the A483 south from Welshpool then, after 5 miles, turn right onto the B4390. Pass through Berriew and Pant-y-Ffridd and the railway is located at Lower House Farm on the outskirts of Manafon.

RHYL MINIATURE RAILWAY

Address: Marine Lake, Wellington Road,
Rhyl   LL18 1AQ
Telephone Nº: (01352) 759109
E-mail: info@rhylminiaturerailway.co.uk
Year Formed: 1911
Location of Line: Rhyl
Length of Line: 1 mile

Nº of Steam Locos: 5
Nº of Other Locos: 3
Nº of Members: Approximately 80
Annual Membership Fee: £8.00
Approx Nº of Visitors P.A.: 20,000
Gauge: 15 inches
Web site: www.rhylminiaturerailway.co.uk

GENERAL INFORMATION

Nearest Mainline Station: Rhyl (1 mile)
Nearest Bus Station: Rhyl (1 mile)
Car Parking: Car Park near the Railway
Coach Parking: Available nearby
Souvenir Shop(s): Yes
Food & Drinks: Available

SPECIAL INFORMATION

The trust operates the oldest Miniature Railway in
the UK. The principal locomotive and train have
been operating there since the 1920's.

OPERATING INFORMATION

Opening Times: 2019 dates: Every weekend from
April until the end of September. Also on Bank
Holiday Mondays and Fridays during June and July
and daily from 12th July to 1st September. Trains
run from 10.30am to 4.00pm. Special Events: Easter
Egg Hunt on 21st & 22nd April, Pirates Weekend
from 25th to 27th May, Teddy Bears Picnic on 3rd &
4th August, Wild West Weekend on 17th & 18th
August and Double Header Day on 26th August.
Steam Working: Every Sunday and also Friday to
Saturday during the School Summer Holidays.
Prices: Adult £3.00
           Child £1.50 (ages 2 to 14)

Detailed Directions by Car:
From All Parts: The Railway is located behind the west end of Rhyl Promenade.

ROMNEY, HYTHE & DYMCHURCH RAILWAY

Address: New Romney Station, New Romney, Kent TN28 8PL	**N° of Steam Locos:** 11
Telephone N°: (01797) 362353	**N° of Other Locos:** 5
E-mail: info@rhdr.org.uk	**N° of Members:** 2,500
Year Formed: 1927	**Annual Membership Fee:** Adult £27.50; Senior/Student £20.00; Junior £10.00
Location of Line: Approximately 5 miles west of Folkestone	**Approx N° of Visitors P.A.:** 160,000
Length of Line: 13½ miles	**Gauge:** 15 inches
	Web site: www.rhdr.org.uk

GENERAL INFORMATION

Nearest Mainline Station: Folkestone Central (5 miles) or Rye
Nearest Bus Station: Folkestone (then take the bus to Hythe)
Car Parking: Free parking at all major stations
Coach Parking: At New Romney & Dungeness
Souvenir Shop(s): Yes – 4 at various stations
Food & Drinks: 2 Cafes serving food and drinks plus a tea shop at Hythe Station.

SPECIAL INFORMATION

Opened in 1927 as 'The World's Smallest Public Railway'. Now the only 15" gauge tourist main line railway in the world. Double track, 7 stations.

OPERATING INFORMATION

Opening Times: 2019 dates: A daily service runs from April to 31st October. Open at weekends in February, March and November and for Santa Specials during December. Also open daily during School half-terms.
Steam Working: All operational days.
Prices: Vary depending on length of journey.
　　Adult Day Rover £18.60
　　Child Day Rover £9.30 (Ages 3-15 years)
　　Concessionary Day Rover £16.60
　　Family Day Rover £49.50
　　　　(2 adults + 3 children)

Detailed Directions by Car:
Exit the M20 at Junction 11 then follow signs to Hythe and the brown tourist signs for the railway. Alternatively, Take the A259 to New Romney and follow the brown tourist signs for the railway.

ROYAL VICTORIA RAILWAY

Address: Royal Victoria Country Park, Netley, Southampton SO31 5GA	**Nº of Steam Locos**: 7
	Nº of Other Locos: 4
Telephone Nº: (023) 8045-6246	**Approx Nº of Visitors P.A.**: Not known
Year Formed: 1995	**Gauge**: 10¼ inches
Location of Line: Netley	**Web site**: www.royalvictoriarailway.co.uk
Length of Line: 1 mile	

GENERAL INFORMATION

Nearest Mainline Station: Netley
Nearest Bus Station: Southampton
Car Parking: Paid parking available on site (using a barrier system)
Coach Parking: None
Food & Drinks: Available in the Country Park

SPECIAL INFORMATION

The railway runs through the grounds of an old Victorian hospital and has good views of the Solent and the Isle of Wight. The Park covers 200 acres including woodland, grassland, beaches, picnic sites and a play area.

OPERATING INFORMATION

Opening Times: Weekends throughout the year and daily during local school holidays. Trains run from 11.00am to 4.30pm. The railway also opens by appointment for larger parties.
Steam Working: On special event days only. Please phone for further details.
Prices: Adult Return £1.75
              Child Return £1.25 (Under-2s ride free)

Detailed Directions by Car:
From All Parts: Exit the M27 at Junction 8 and follow the Brown Tourist signs for the Royal Victoria Country Park. You will reach the Park after approximately 3 miles. Do not use Sat Nav as the directions will be incorrect!

RUDYARD LAKE STEAM RAILWAY

Address: Rudyard Station, Rudyard, Near Leek, Staffordshire ST13 8PF	**N⁰ of Steam Locos:** 6
Telephone N⁰: (01538) 306704	**N⁰ of Other Locos:** 4
Year Formed: 1985	**Approx N⁰ of Visitors P.A.:** 50,000
Location: Rudyard to Hunthouse Wood	**Gauge:** 10¼ inches
Length of Line: 1½ miles	**Web site:** www.rlsr.org

GENERAL INFORMATION

Nearest Mainline Station: Stoke-on-Trent (10 miles)
Nearest Bus Station: Leek
Car Parking: Free parking at Rudyard Station
Coach Parking: Free parking at Rudyard Station
Souvenir Shop(s): Yes
Food & Drinks: Cafe open daily 10.00am to 4.00pm

SPECIAL INFORMATION

The Railway runs along the side of the historic Rudyard Lake that gave author Rudyard Kipling his name. "Drive a Steam Train" courses can be booked or bought as a gift with vouchers valid for 12 months.

OPERATING INFORMATION

Opening Times: 2019 dates: Every weekend and Bank Holiday from 30th March to the 3rd November and daily during all the local school holidays.
Steam Working: All trains are normally steam hauled. Trains run from 11.00am and the last train runs at 4.00pm. A round trip lasts 45 minutes.
Prices: Adult Return £5.00
Child Return £3.00 (Under-3s ride free)
Other fares and Day Rover tickets are also available.

Detailed Directions by Car:
From All Parts: Head for Leek then follow the A523 North towards Macclesfield for 1 mile. Follow the brown tourist signs to the B5331 signposted for Rudyard for ½ mile. Pass under the Railway bridge and turn immediately left and go up the ramp to the Station car park.

RUISLIP LIDO RAILWAY

Address: Reservoir Road, Ruislip,
Middlesex HA4 7TY
Telephone Nº: (01895) 622595
Year Formed: 1979
Location of Line: Trains travel from
Ruislip Lido to Woody Bay
Length of Line: 1¼ miles

Nº of Steam Locos: 1
Nº of Other Locos: 5
Approximate Nº of Members: 170
Annual Membership Fee: £20.00 (Adult)
Approx Nº of Visitors P.A.: 60,000
Gauge: 12 inches
Web site: www.ruisliplidorailway.org

GENERAL INFORMATION

Nearest Mainline Station: West Ruislip (2 miles)
Nearest Bus Station: Ruislip Underground Station
Car Parking: Free parking available at the Lido
Coach Parking: Free parking available at the Lido
Souvenir Shop(s): Yes
Food & Drinks: A Cafe is open on weekends and
Bank Holidays. A Pub/Restaurant is open daily.

SPECIAL INFORMATION

The steam locomotive, 'Mad Bess' used by Ruislip
Lido Railway was actually built by the members over
a 12 year period!

OPERATING INFORMATION

Opening Times: 2019 dates: Weekends from 16th
February to 24th November. Daily from 20th July to
1st September. Please contact the railway for details
about other services running during November,
December and January.
Steam Working: Most weekends from May to
September.
Prices: Adult Return £3.30 (Single fare £2.20)
Child Return £2.80 (Single fare £1.70)
Family Return £11.00 (Single fare £7.00)
(2 adults + 2 children)
Note: Under-3s travel for free

Detailed Directions by Car:
From All Parts: Follow the signs from the A40 and take the A4180 through Ruislip before turning left onto the
B469.

SALTBURN MINIATURE RAILWAY

Address: Valley Gardens, Saltburn
Telephone Nº: (01287) 622712
Year Formed: 1947
Location of Line: Cat Nab to Forest Halt
Stations, Saltburn
Length of Line: ¾ mile
Web site: www.saltburn-miniature-railway.org.uk

Nº of Steam Locos: 1
Nº of Other Locos: 3
Nº of Members: 12
Annual Membership Fee: £1.00
Approx Nº of Visitors P.A.: 20,000
Gauge: 15 inches

OPERATING INFORMATION

Opening Times: Weekends and Bank Holidays from Easter until the end of September. Also open Tuesday to Friday during the Summer School Holidays. All services operate weather permitting. Trains run from 1.00pm to 5.00pm.
Steam Working: Please contact the railway for details.
Prices: Adult Return £2.00 (Adult Single £1.00)
Child Return 1.00 (Child Single 50p)
Note: Family tickets and frequent user discounts are also available. Under-5s ride free of charge.

GENERAL INFORMATION

Nearest Mainline Station: Saltburn (½ mile)
Nearest Bus Station: Saltburn (½ mile)
Car Parking: Available at Cat Nab Station
Coach Parking: Glen Side (at the top of the bank)
Souvenir Shop(s): At Cat Nab Station
Food & Drinks: None

E-mail: info@saltburn-miniature-railway@org.uk

Detailed Directions by Car:
Follow the A174 from Middlesbrough (West) or Whitby (East) to Saltburn-by-the-Sea. Cat Nab Station with its adjoining car park is situated by the beach, directly off the C74 (C174).

SHERWOOD FOREST RAILWAY

Address: Gorsethorpe Lane, Edwinstowe, Mansfield   NG21 9HL
Telephone Nº: (01623) 515339
Year Formed: 1999
Location of Line: Between Mansfield Woodhouse and Edwinstowe
Length of Line: 680 yards

Nº of Steam Locos: 2
Nº of Other Locos: 3
Nº of Members: 13
Approx Nº of Visitors P.A.: 5,000
Gauge: 15 inches
Website: www.sherwoodforestrailway.com

GENERAL INFORMATION

Nearest Mainline Station: Mansfield (7 miles)
Nearest Bus Station: Mansfield (7 miles)
Car Parking: Free parking available on site
Coach Parking: Available on site
Souvenir Shop(s): Yes
Food & Drinks: Available

SPECIAL INFORMATION

The Railway runs through the grounds of Shaw-Browne Estates which has play areas for children and picnic areas. Check out the web site for up-to-date news.

OPERATING INFORMATION

Opening Times: 2019 dates: Open daily from 17th February through to the end of November. Trains run from 11.00am to dusk on most days.
Steam Working: Every operating day.
Prices: Adults £2.00
             Chidren £2.00

Detailed Directions by Car:
From the A1: Turn off at the Worksop roundabout and head to Ollerton. Follow the A6075 through Edwinstowe and towards Mansfield Woodhouse, then turn left at the double mini-roundabout. The railway is on the right after approximately 200 yards; From Nottingham: Head to Ollerton, then as above; From the M1: Exit at Junction 27 and head into Mansfield. Follow signs to Mansfield Woodhouse and then on towards Edwinstowe. From here, follow the tourist signs for the Steam Railway.

SITTINGBOURNE & KEMSLEY LIGHT RAILWAY

Address: The Wall, Sittingbourne Retail Park, Sittingbourne, Kent ME10 2XD
Info/Talking Timetable: (01795) 424899
Contact Nº: 07973 192938
Year Formed: 1969
Location of Line: North of Sittingbourne
Length of Line: 2 miles

Nº of Steam Locos: 9 (2 Standard gauge)
Nº of Other Locos: 3
Nº of Members: 300
Annual Membership Fee: £20.00
Approx Nº of Visitors P.A.: 7,000
Gauge: 2 feet 6 inches
Web site: www.sklr.net

GENERAL INFORMATION

Nearest Mainline Station: Sittingbourne (¼ mile)
Nearest Bus Station: Sittingbourne Mainline station
Car Parking: Sittingbourne Retail Park (behind KFC)
Coach Parking: Sittingbourne Retail Park
Souvenir Shop(s): Yes
Food & Drinks: Yes

SPECIAL INFORMATION

The railway is the only original preserved narrow gauge industrial steam railway in S.E. England (once the Bowaters Paper Company Railway). The first kilometre of the line passes over the century-old Milton Regis Viaduct before crossing Milton Creek Country Park to the operational paper mill and Kemsley Down. Other attractions include a Museum, garden railway, Children's play area & Wildlife Garden.

OPERATING INFORMATION

Opening Times: 2019 dates: Sundays and Bank Holiday weekends from Easter to 29th September. Also open on Wednesdays in August and for Santa Specials on weekends from 30th November to 22nd December. Please visit the web site for details of other Special Events held throughout the year.
Steam Working: Trains run from 1.00pm normally, but from 11.00am on Bank Holiday weekends and Sundays in August. Last train runs at 4.00pm (except for during some special events).
Prices: Adult Return £7.00
          Child Return £3.50 (Under-3s ride free)
          Senior Citizen Return £6.00
          Family Return £20.00 (2 Adult + 4 Child)
Note: Different fares may apply on special event days.

Detailed Directions by Car:
From East or West: Take the M2 (or M20) to the A249 and travel towards Sittingbourne. Exit onto the B2006 signposted for Bobbing and continue along the B2006 into the town centre. At the roundabout by the garage turn right into Mill Way (signposted for Kent Science Park) and then follow the brown heritage signs into Sittingbourne Retail Park for the railway. Free parking is available behind KFC and opposite Pizza Hut.

SNOWDON MOUNTAIN RAILWAY

Address: Llanberis, Caernarfon, Gwynedd, Wales LL55 4TY	**Length of Line**: 4¾ miles
Telephone Nº: (01286) 870223	**Nº of Steam Locos**: 4
Fax Nº: (01286) 872518	**Nº of Other Locos**: 4
Year Formed: 1894	**Approx Nº of Visitors P.A.**: 140,000
Location of Line: Llanberis to the summit of Snowdon	**Gauge**: 2 feet 7½ inches
	Web site: www.snowdonrailway.co.uk

GENERAL INFORMATION

Nearest Mainline Station: Bangor (9 miles)
Nearest Bus Station: Caernarfon (7½ miles)
Car Parking: Llanberis Station car park – pay and display. Also other car parks nearby.
Coach Parking: As above, but space is very limited.
Souvenir Shop(s): Yes
Food & Drinks: Yes

SPECIAL INFORMATION

Britain's only public rack and pinion railway climbs to within 60 feet of the 3,560 feet (1,085 metre) peak of Snowdon, the highest mountain in England and Wales. The Diesel and Steam Experiences are both 2½ hour return journeys to the summit.

OPERATING INFORMATION

Opening Times: Open daily (weather permitting) from mid-March until the end of October. Trains depart at regular intervals from 9.00am. The last departure can be as late as 5.30pm depending on demand. It is advisable to guarantee tickets and book in advance either online or by telephone.
Steam Working: Ride the "Snowdon Lily" or the "Mountain Goat" as part of the Heritage Steam Experience operating from May to September. Please contact the railway for further details.
Prices: Adult Summit Return £30.00 (Diesel)
Adult Summit Return £39.00 (Steam)
Child Summit Return £21.00 (Diesel)
Child Summit Return £29.00 (Steam)
Note: During March and April, trains only travel up as far as Clogwyn, ¾ of the way up the mountain.

Detailed Directions by Car:
Llanberis Station is situated on the A4086 Caernarfon to Capel Curig road, 7½ miles from Caernarfon. Convenient access via the main North Wales coast road (A55). Exit at the A55/A5 junction and follow signs to Llanberis via B4366, B4547 and A4086.

SOUTH DOWNS LIGHT RAILWAY

Address: South Downs Light Railway, Stopham Road, Pulborough RH20 1DS **Telephone Nº**: 07518 753784 **Year Formed**: 1999 **Location**: Pulborough Garden Centre **Length of Line**: 1 kilometre	**Nº of Steam Locos**: 7 **Nº of Other Locos**: 2 **Nº of Members**: 60 **Annual Membership Fee**: Adult £20.00 **Approx Nº of Visitors P.A.**: 20,000 **Gauge**: 10¼ inches **Web site**: www.south-downs-railway.com

GENERAL INFORMATION

Nearest Mainline Station: Pulborough (½ mile)
Nearest Bus Station: Bus stop just outside Centre
Car Parking: Free parking on site
Coach Parking: Free parking on site
Souvenir Shop(s): Yes
Food & Drinks: Yes – in the Garden Restaurant

SPECIAL INFORMATION

The members of the Society own and operate a large collection of 10¼ inch gauge locomotives.
The Railway is located within the Pulborough Garden Centre.

OPERATING INFORMATION

Opening Times: Weekends and Bank Holidays from March until September, Wednesdays in School Holidays and also Santa Specials at weekends in December. Trains run from 11.00am to 3.30pm.
Steam Working: Most services are steam hauled.
Prices: Adult £2.00
            Child £1.00 (Under-2s travel free of charge)
Note: Supersaver tickets are also available and a special 'South Downs Belle' runs on the first Sunday of each month.

Detailed Directions by Car:
From All Parts: The Centre is situated on the A283, ½ mile west of Pulborough. Pulborough itself is on the A29 London to Bognor Regis Road.

SOUTHEND PIER RAILWAY

Address: Western Esplanade, Southend-on-Sea SS1 1EE	**Nº of Steam Locos**: None
Telephone Nº: (01702) 215620	**Nº of Other Locos**: 2
Year Formed: 1889	**Approx Nº of Visitors P.A.**: 300,000
Location of Line: Southend seafront	**Gauge**: 3 feet
Length of Line: 2,180 yards	**Web site**: www.visitsouthend.co.uk/ things-to-do/2449/southendpier/

GENERAL INFORMATION

Nearest Mainline Station: Southend Central (¼ mile)
Nearest Bus Station: Southend (¼ mile)
Car Parking: Available on the seafront
Coach Parking: Available
Souvenir Shop(s): Yes
Food & Drinks: Available

SPECIAL INFORMATION

The railway takes passengers to the end of Southend Pier which, at 1.33 miles, is the longest pleasure pier in the world.

OPERATING INFORMATION

Opening Times: Most days except for Christmas Day and on Mondays and Tuesdays during the winter months when the pier itself is closed. Times vary depending on the season – trains run from 8.15am to 8.00pm during the Summer and generally from 9.15am to 5.00pm in the Winter.
Steam Working: None.
Prices: Adult Return £5.35
　　　　　Child Return £2.65
　　　　　Concessionary Return £2.65
　　　　　Family Return Ticket £13.50

Detailed Directions by Car:
From All Parts: Take the A127 to Southend and follow the brown tourist signs to the Pier.

SOUTH TYNEDALE RAILWAY

Address: The Railway Station, Alston,
Cumbria   CA9 3JB
Telephone Nº: (01434) 382828
Year Formed: 1973
Location of Line: From Alston, northwards
along South Tyne Valley to Slaggyford
Length of Line: 5 miles

Nº of Steam Locos: 4
Nº of Other Locos: 4
Nº of Members: 300
Annual Membership Fee: £22.00 (Adult)
Approx Nº of Visitors P.A.: 22,000
Gauge: 2 feet
Web: www.south-tynedale-railway.org.uk

GENERAL INFO

Nearest Mainline Station:
Haltwhistle (15 miles)
Nearest Bus Stop:
Alston Townfoot (¼ mile)
Car Parking: Free parking at
Alston Station but limited spaces
available at Lintley & Slaggyford
Coach Parking: Free parking at
Alston & Slaggyford Stations but
a drop off point only at Lintley
Souvenir Shop(s): Yes – at
Alston & Slaggyford Stations
Food & Drinks: Available at
Alston & Slaggyford Stations

SPECIAL INFO

The railway runs along part of the
old Alston to Haltwhistle branch
line in the South Tyne Valley.

OPERATING INFO

Opening Times: 2019 dates:
Bank Holidays, weekends,
Tuesdays, Thursdays and daily
during School Holidays between
30th March and 31st October.
Please check the railway's website
for information about other
running dates including Special
Events including Halloween and
Santa Specials.
Steam Working: Please contact
the railway for details.
Prices: Adult Day Rover £10.00
Adult Single £8.00
Child Day Rover £5.00
Child Single £4.00
(Under-1s travel free)
Family Rover £25.00
(2 Adults + 3 Children)
Dogs £2.00

Detailed Directions by Car:
Alston can be reached by a number of roads from various directions including A689, A686 and the B6277. Alston
Station is situated just off the A686 Hexham road, north of Alston Town Centre. Look for the brown tourist signs
on roads into Alston.   Slaggyford Station is signposted off the A689.

STEEPLE GRANGE LIGHT RAILWAY

Address: Old Porter Lane, Steeple Grange, Wirksworth   DE4 4GE
Telephone Nº: (01629) 55123 (Evenings)
Year Formed: 1986
Location of Line: Adjacent to the High Peak trail near Wirksworth
Length of Line: ½ mile at present

Nº of Steam Locos: None
Nº of Other Locos: 16
Nº of Members: 200
Annual Membership Fee: From £8.00
Approx Nº of Visitors P.A.: 8,000+
Gauge: 18 inches
Web site: www.steeplegrange.co.uk

GENERAL INFORMATION

Nearest Mainline Station: Cromford (2 miles)
Nearest Bus Station: Matlock
Car Parking: Free parking in Old Porter Lane, plus other Pay and Display car parks nearby.
Coach Parking: Available nearby
Souvenir Shop(s): Yes
Food & Drinks: Light refreshments available

SPECIAL INFORMATION

The Railway is built on the track bed of the former Standard Gauge Cromford and High Peak Railway branch to Middleton. The railway uses mostly former mining/quarrying rolling stock and has two separate lines operating.

OPERATING INFORMATION

Opening Times: Sundays and Bank Holidays from Easter until the end of September. Also open on Saturdays in July and August and on other days by prior arrangement. Special Events at other times of the year including Santa Specials during December. Please contact the railway for further information. Trains run from 12.00pm to 4.30pm
Steam Working: None
Prices: Adult Return £5.00   Child Return £3.00
   Senior Citizen Return £4.00
   Family Return £15.00
Note: Special fares apply during special events and also for group bookings.

Detailed Directions by Car:
The Railway is situated adjacent to the National Stone Centre just to the north of Wirksworth at the junction of the B5035 and B5036.

SUTTON HALL RAILWAY

Address: Tabors Farm, Sutton Hall, Shopland Road, near Rochford, Essex SS4 1LQ	**N° of Steam Locos**: 1
	N° of Other Locos: 1
	Approx N° of Visitors P.A.: 3,500
Telephone N°: 07947 280573	**Gauge**: 10¼ inches
Year Formed: 1997	**Web site**: None at present
Location of Line: Sutton Hall Farm	
Length of Line: Almost 1 mile	

GENERAL INFO

Nearest Mainline Station:
Southend Airport (2 miles)
Nearest Bus Station: Rochford
Car Parking:
Free parking available on site
Coach Parking:
Free parking available on site
Souvenir Shop(s): None
Food & Drinks:
Drinks and snacks available

SPECIAL INFORMATION

The Railway was bought by C. Tabor in 1985 for use with his Farm Barn Dances. The Sutton Hall Railway Society was formed in 1997 (with C. Tabor as Society President) and now opens the line for public running on some Sundays. The railway is staffed entirely by Volunteer Members of the Society.

OPERATING INFO

Opening Times: Open the 4th Sunday in the month from April until September, 12.00pm to 4.00pm. Also open on Easter Sunday 12.00pm to 4.00pm and the first Sunday in December, 12.00pm to 4.00pm.
Steam Working: All operating days.
Prices: Adults £2.00 per ride
Children £1.50 per ride
Note: The railway is also available to hire for private events.

Detailed Directions by Car:
From Southend Airport (A127 Southend to London Main Route & A1159): At the Airport Roundabout (with the McDonalds on the left) go over the railway bridge signposted for Rochford. At the 1st roundabout turn right (Ann Boleyn Pub on the right) into Sutton Road. Continue straight on at the mini-roundabout then when the road forks turn left into Shopland Road signposted for Barling and Great Wakering. Turn right after approximately 400 yards into the long tree-lined road for Sutton Hall Farm.

TALYLLYN RAILWAY

Address: Wharf Station, Tywyn, Gwynedd, LL36 9EY	**N° of Steam Locos**: 6
Telephone N°: (01654) 710472	**N° of Other Locos**: 4
E-mail: enquiries@talyllyn.co.uk	**N° of Members**: 3,500
Year Formed: 1865	**Annual Membership Fee**: Adult £30.00
Location of Line: Tywyn to Nant Gwernol	**Approx N° of Visitors P.A.**: 40,000
Length of Line: 7¼ miles	**Gauge**: 2 feet 3 inches
	Web site: www.talyllyn.co.uk

GENERAL INFORMATION

Nearest Mainline Station: Tywyn (300 yards)
Nearest Bus Station: Tywyn (300 yards)
Car Parking: 100 yards away
Coach Parking: Free parking (100 yards)
Souvenir Shop(s): Yes
Food & Drinks: Yes

SPECIAL INFORMATION

Talyllyn Railway was the first preserved railway in the world – saved from closure in 1951. The railway was originally opened in 1866 to carry slate from Bryn Eglwys Quarry to Tywyn. Among the railway's attractions are a Narrow Gauge Railway Museum at the Tywyn Wharf terminus.
See us on facebook and twitter!

OPERATING INFORMATION

Opening Times: 2019 dates: Daily from 1st April to 3rd November. Also open on other selected dates in January, February, March and December. Generally open from 10.30am to 5.00pm. Please contact the railway or check their web site for further details.
Steam Working: All services are steam-hauled.
Prices: Adult Return £17.70 (Day Rover ticket) Children (ages 5-15) pay £4.50 if travelling with an adult. Otherwise, they pay half adult fare. Children under the age of 5 travel free of charge.
Note: The prices shown are for Standard tickets though passengers are encouraged to consider paying for slightly more expensive Gift Aid tickets.

Detailed Directions by Car:
From the North: Take the A493 from Dolgellau into Tywyn; From the South: Take the A493 from Machynlleth to Tywyn.

TEIFI VALLEY RAILWAY

Address: Henllan Station, Henllan, near Newcastle Emlyn   SA44 5TD
Telephone Nº: (01559) 371077
Year Formed: 1978
Location of Line: Between Cardigan and Carmarthen off the A484
Length of Line: A third of a mile at present (in the process of being extended)

Nº of Steam Locos: 2
Nº of Other Locos: 3
Nº of Members: Approximately 150
Annual Membership Fee: £18.00
Approx Nº of Visitors P.A.: 15,000
Gauge: 2 feet
Web site: www.teifivalleyrailway.wales
Facebook: facebook.com/TeifiValleyRly

GENERAL INFORMATION

Nearest Mainline Station: Carmarthen (10 miles)
Nearest Bus Station: Carmarthen (10 miles)
Car Parking: Spaces for 70 cars available.
Coach Parking: Spaces for 4 coaches available.
Souvenir Shop(s): Yes
Food & Drinks: Yes – Cafe is open on weekends

SPECIAL INFORMATION

The Railway was formerly part of the G.W.R. but now runs on a Narrow Gauge using Quarry Engines.

OPERATING INFORMATION

Opening Times: 2019 dates: Open daily from 7th to 28th April then every Wednesday and Sunday until the 8th September. Also open daily from 26th May to 2nd June and from 14th July to 8th September. Santa Specials operate on dates during December. Please contact the railway for further details. Trains run from 11.00am to 4.00pm.
Steam Working: Most operating days – please phone the Railway for further details.
Prices: Adult £3.00
          Child £3.00

Detailed Directions by Car:
From All Parts: The Railway is situated in the Village of Henllan between the A484 and the A475 (on the B4334) about 4 miles east of Newcastle Emlyn.

THRELKELD QUARRY RAILWAY

Address: Threlkeld Quarry & Mining Museum, Threlkeld, Near Keswick, CA12 4TT
Telephone Nº: (01768) 779747
Year Formed: 2010
Web site: www.threlkeldquarryandminingmuseum.co.uk
E-mail: threlkeldquarrymuseum@btconnect.com

Nº of Steam Locos: 1   **Other Locos:** 2
Approx Nº of Visitors P.A.: 20,000
Gauge: 2 feet
Location of Line: Cumbria
Length of Line: ½ mile

GENERAL INFORMATION

Nearest Mainline Station: Penrith (14 miles)
Nearest Bus Station: Keswick (5 miles)
Car Parking: Available on site
Coach Parking: Available
Souvenir Shop(s): Yes
Food & Drinks: Available

SPECIAL INFORMATION

Underground tours (over-5s only) are available for an extra charge. Demonstration Working Weekends in conjunction with the Vintage Excavator Trust are held on the third weekend in May and September.

OPERATING INFORMATION

Opening Times: Daily from Easter to the end of October half-term. Santa Specials also run on dates in December. Please contact the Museum for details. Open from 10.00am to 5.00pm.
Steam Working: During the School Holidays and on Bank Holiday weekends. A Steam Gala is held on the last weekend in July.
Prices: Adult Museum Entry £3.00   Rides £3.00
          Child Museum Entry £1.50   Rides £1.50
An Annual Family Pass which includes admission and rides is £35.00 (2 adults + 2 children)

Detailed Directions by Car:
From All Parts: Exit the M6 at Junction 40 and take the A66 towards Keswick. Turn off onto the B5322 at Threlkeld and follow signs for the Mining Museum.

TODDINGTON NARROW GAUGE RAILWAY

Address: The Station, Toddington, Cheltenham, Gloucestershire   GL54 5DT
Telephone Nº: (01242) 621405
Year Formed: 1985
Location of Line: 5 miles south of Broadway, Worcestershire, near the A46
Length of Line: ½ mile
Web site: www.toddington-narrow-gauge.co.uk

Nº of Steam Locos: 4
Nº of Other Locos: 7
Nº of Members: Approximately 50
Annual Membership Fee: £10.00
Approx Nº of Visitors P.A.: 2,000
Gauge: 2 feet

GENERAL INFORMATION

Nearest Mainline Station: Cheltenham Spa or Ashchurch
Nearest Bus Station: Cheltenham
Car Parking: Parking available at Toddington
Coach Parking: Parking available as above
Souvenir Shop(s): None
Food & Drinks: None at the TNGR itself but available at the adjacent GWSR site.

SPECIAL INFORMATION

The railway is situated in the car park of Toddington Station on the Gloucestershire Warwickshire Railway.

OPERATING INFORMATION

Opening Times: 2019 dates: Most Sundays and Bank Holidays from 21st April to 20th October inclusive and also on Wednesdays during August. A number of Special Event weekends operate throughout the season. Please check the railway's web site for details. Trains usually run every 35 minutes from 11.45am to 3.50pm.
Steam Working: Please check the web site for further information.
Prices: Adults £4.00
             Children £2.00 (Under-5s ride free)

Detailed Directions by Car:
Toddington is 11 miles north east of Cheltenham, 5 miles south of Broadway just off the B4632 (old A46). Exit the M5 at Junction 9 towards Stow-on-the-Wold for the B4632. The Railway is clearly visible from the B4632.

VALE OF RHEIDOL RAILWAY

Address: Park Avenue, Aberystwyth, Ceredigion SY23 1PG	**Nº of Steam Locos:** 6 (3 in regular service)
Telephone Nº: (01970) 625819	**Nº of Other Locos:** 1
Year Formed: 1897 (Opened in 1902)	**Gauge:** 1 foot 11¾ inches
Location: Aberystwyth to Devil's Bridge	**Web site:** www.rheidolrailway.co.uk
Length of Line: 11¾ miles	**E-mail:** info@rheidolrailway.co.uk

GENERAL INFORMATION

Nearest Mainline Station: Aberystwyth (adjacent)
Nearest Bus Station: Aberystwyth (adjacent)
Car Parking: Available on site
Coach Parking: Parking available on site
Souvenir Shops: At Devil's Bridge and Aberystwyth
Food & Drinks: At Devil's Bridge and Aberystwyth

SPECIAL INFORMATION

The journey between the stations take one hour in each direction. At Devil's Bridge there is a cafe, toilets, a picnic area and the famous Mynach Falls. The line climbs over 600 feet in 11¾ miles. Look out for the Red Kites and Buzzards flying overhead! "Driver for a Fiver" operates at Devil's Bridge on certain days during the summer months.

OPERATING INFORMATION

Opening Times: 2019 dates: Services run daily from 16th to 28th February, weekends during March and daily from 30th March to 1st November, then Sundays only for the rest of November. Santa Trains operate on dates during December. Please check the web site or phone the railway for further details.
Steam Working: All trains are steam-hauled.
Prices: Adult Return £23.00
Senior Citizen Return £23.00
Child Return £10.00
Family Return £55.00 (2 adult + 2 child)
Family Return £37.00 (1 adult + 2 child)
Note: Family tickets are also available for larger families. Trains can be chartered by arrangement at other times of the year. Please e-mail for details.

Detailed Directions by Car:
From the North take A487 into Aberystwyth. From the East take A470 and A44 to Aberystwyth. From the South take A487 or A485 to Aberystwyth. The Station is located in the centre of town near the 'Park and Ride' site. Follow the brown tourist signs from the edge of town.

WATFORD MINIATURE RAILWAY

Address: Cassiobury Park, Watford, WD17 7LB
Telephone Nº: (01525) 854609
Year Formed: 1959
Location: At the northern end of Cassiobury Park, Watford
Length of Line: 600 yards

Nº of Steam Locos: 1
Nº of Other Locos: 4
Approx Nº of Visitors P.A.: Not known
Gauge: 10¼ inches
Web site: www.watfordrailway.co.uk
E-mail: watford@minirail.co.uk

GENERAL INFORMATION

Nearest Mainline Station: Watford Junction (appoximately 1½ miles)
Nearest Tube Station: Watford (400 yards)
Car Parking: Limited spaces available at the Park.
Coach Parking: None
Souvenir Shop(s): None
Food & Drinks: Cafe available in the Park.

OPERATING INFORMATION

Opening Times: 2019 dates: Weekends and School Holidays from January to November inclusive and daily from 6th April to 29th September. Also open from 26th to 31st December and during the first week in January. Open between 11.00am and 5.00pm throughout most of the year but from 12.00pm to 4.00pm in January, February and from late October to the end of the year. Please check the web site for further information.
Steam Working: To be confirmed. Steam running dates will be published on the web site.
Prices: All fares: £2.00 per ride (Under-2s free)

Detailed Directions by Car:
Exit the M25 at Junction 19 or 20 and follow the A41 to Watford. Turn right at the Dome Roundabout heading southwards on the A412 St. Albans Road and continue through Watford Town Centre onto the A412 Rickmansworth Road. Turn right onto Cassiobury Park Avenue, following the brown information sign and continue to the end of the road for the car park.

WAT TYLER MINIATURE RAILWAY

Address: Pitsea Hall Lane, Pitsea, Basildon   SS16 4UH
Telephone Nº: (01268) 275050
Year Formed: 1988
Location of Line: Basildon, Essex
Length of Line: 1 mile
Web site: www.wattylercountrypark.org.uk/mini-rail

Nº of Steam Locos: None
Nº of Other Locos: 2
Approx Nº of Visitors P.A.: 200,000 visitors to the Park – 20,000 rides
Gauge: 10¼ inches

GENERAL INFORMATION

Nearest Mainline Station: East Pitsea (½ mile)
Nearest Bus Station: Basildon (2 miles)
Car Parking: Available on site
Coach Parking: Available
Souvenir Shop(s): None
Food & Drinks: Available

SPECIAL INFORMATION

The railway is located in the Wat Tyler Country Park close to the site of a 19th Century explosives factory.

OPERATING INFORMATION

Opening Times: Weekends and Bank Holidays throughout the year and daily during School Holidays. Open 12.00am to 5.00pm in the Summer and from 12.00pm to 3.00pm in the Winter months.
Steam Working: None
Prices: Adult Return £2.50
   Child Return £1.50

Detailed Directions by Car:
From All Parts: Exit the A13 at the Pitsea Flyover and follow signs for Wat Tyler Country Park which is approximately ½ mile on the right.

WELLINGTON COUNTRY PARK RAILWAY

Address: Odiham Road, Riseley, RG7 1SP
Telephone Nº: (0118) 932-6444
Year Formed: 1980
Location of Line: Riseley, Berkshire
Length of Line: 500 yards
Web site: www.wellington-country-park.co.uk

Nº of Steam Locos: None
Nº of Other Locos: 1
Approx Nº of Visitors P.A.: 140,000+ (to the Country Park)
Gauge: 12¼ inches

GENERAL INFORMATION

Nearest Mainline Station: Mortimer (5 miles)
Nearest Bus Station: Reading (9 miles)
Car Parking: Available on site
Coach Parking: Available
Souvenir Shop(s): Yes
Food & Drinks: Available

SPECIAL INFORMATION

The railway is located within 350 acres of beautiful parklands which surround a 35 acre lake. The line itself has recently been converted from a 7¼ inch gauge to a 12¼ inch gauge.

OPERATING INFORMATION

Opening Times: 2019 dates: Daily from 16th February until 4th November. Open from 9.30am to 5.30pm (but until 4.30pm during the Winter).
Steam Working: None
Prices: Adults £13.50 (Park Admission)
Children £13.50 (Park Admission)
Under-3s are admitted free
Family Tickets £51.50
(2 adults + 2 children)
Note: Train rides are an additional £1.00 each (though Under-3s ride for free).

Detailed Directions by Car:
From All Parts: Exit the M4 at Junction 11 and take the A33 towards Basingstoke. Turn onto the B3349 at the Riseley roundabout and follow the signs to the Park which is straight off the roundabout.

WELLS HARBOUR RAILWAY

Address: Wells Harbour Railway,
Pinewoods, Beach Road,
Wells-next-the-Sea   NR23 1DR
Telephone Nº: (07939) 149264
Year Formed: 1976
Location of Line: Wells-next-the-Sea
Length of Line: Approximately 1 mile

Nº of Steam Locos: None
Nº of Other Locos: 3
Approx Nº of Visitors P.A.: 50,000
Gauge: 10¼ inches
Web site: None

GENERAL INFORMATION

Nearest Mainline Station: King's Lynn (21 miles)
Nearest Bus Station: Norwich (24 miles)
Car Parking: Public car parks near each station
Coach Parking: Available in town
Souvenir Shop(s): No
Food & Drinks: No

SPECIAL INFORMATION

Wells Harbour Railway was the first 10¼" narrow
gauge railway to run a scheduled passenger service
and is listed in the Guinness Book of Records!

OPERATING INFORMATION

Opening Times: Weekends from Easter until Spring
Bank Holiday then daily through to the middle of
September. Then weekends until the end of October.
The first train departs at 10.30am.
Steam Working: None
Prices: £1.50 per ride

Detailed Directions by Car:
Wells-next-the-Sea is located on the North Norfolk cost between Hunstanton and Cromer. The railway is situated
on Beach Road next to the harbour. Follow the signs for Pinewoods and Beach.

WELLS & WALSINGHAM LIGHT RAILWAY

Address: Stiffkey Road, Wells-next-the-Sea, NR23 1QB
Telephone Nº: (01328) 711630
Year Formed: 1982
Location of Line: Wells-next-the-Sea to Walsingham, Norfolk
Length of Line: 4 miles

Nº of Steam Locos: 2
Nº of Other Locos: 2
Nº of Members: 50
Annual Membership Fee: £21.00
Approx Nº of Visitors P.A.: 33,000
Gauge: 10¼ inches
Website: www.wwlr.co.uk

GENERAL INFORMATION

Nearest Mainline Station: King's Lynn (21 miles)
Nearest Bus Station: Norwich (24 miles)
Car Parking: Free parking at site
Coach Parking: Free parking at site
Souvenir Shop(s): Yes
Food & Drinks: Yes

SPECIAL INFORMATION

The Railway is the longest 10¼ inch narrow-gauge steam railway in the world. The course of the railway is famous for wildlife and butterflies in season.

OPERATING INFORMATION

Opening Times: 2019 dates: Daily from 3rd March until 3rd November.
Steam Working: Most operating days with a diesel service on Mondays except for during the school holidays. Trains run from 10.30am on most days (10.00am during the school summer holidays).
Prices: Adult Return £9.50
Child Return £7.50 (Under-4s ride free)

Detailed Directions by Car:
Wells-next-the-Sea is situated on the North Norfolk Coast midway between Hunstanton and Cromer. The Main Station is situated on the main A149 Stiffkey Road. Follow the brown tourist signs for the Railway.

WELSH HIGHLAND HERITAGE RAILWAY

Address: Tremadog Road, Porthmadog, Gwynedd LL49 9DY	**Nº of Steam Locos:** 5
Telephone Nº: (01766) 513402	**Nº of Other Locos:** 19
Year Formed: 1961	**Nº of Members:** 1,000
Location of Line: Opposite Porthmadog Mainline Station	**Annual Membership Fee:** £30.00 Adult
	Approx Nº of Visitors P.A.: 25,000
Length of Line: 1½ mile round trip	**Gauge:** 1 foot 11½ inches
	Web site: www.whr.co.uk

GENERAL INFORMATION

Nearest Mainline Station: Porthmadog (adjacent)
Nearest Bus Station: Services 1 & 3 stop 50 yards away
Car Parking: Free parking at site, plus a public Pay and Display car park within 100 yards
Coach Parking: Adjacent
Souvenir Shop(s): Yes – large range available
Food & Drinks: Yes – excellent home cooking at the Russell Team Room!

SPECIAL INFORMATION

The Welsh Highland Railway is a family-orientated attraction based around a Railway Heritage Centre and includes a guided, hands-on tour of the sheds.

OPERATING INFORMATION

Opening Times: 2019 dates: Daily from 4th May to 2nd November except for most Mondays and Fridays in May, June, September and October. Also open daily during local school holidays and at weekends during April. Trains run from 10.30am to 4.00pm.
Steam Working: Most days during the School Holidays and on other selected weekends. Please check with the railway for further details.
Prices: Adult Day Rover £9.50
           Child Day Rover £4.75 (Under-3s free)
           Family Day Rover £25.00
                (2 adults + 2 children)

Detailed Directions by Car:
From Bangor/Caernarfon take the A487 to Porthmadog. From Pwllheli take the A497 to Porthmadog then turn left at the roundabout. From the Midlands take A487 to Portmadog. Once in Porthmadog, follow the brown tourist signs. The line is located right next to Porthmadog Mainline Station, opposite the Queens Hotel.

WELSH HIGHLAND RAILWAY

Postal Address: Ffestiniog Railway, Harbour Station, Porthmadog LL49 9NF	**N° of Steam Locos:** 8 (5 working)
Telephone N°: (01766) 516000	**N° of Other Locos:** 3
Year Formed: 1997	**N° of Members:** 2,300
Location: Caernarfon to Porthmadog	**Annual Membership Fee:** £39.00
Length of Line: 25 miles	**Approx N° of Visitors P.A.:** 360,000
E-mail: enquiries@festrail.co.uk	**Gauge:** 1 foot 11½ inches
	Web site: www.festrail.co.uk

GENERAL INFORMATION

Nearest Mainline Station:
Porthmadog (½ mile) or Bangor (7 miles)
(Bus service N° 5 to Caernarfon)
Nearest Bus Station:
Porthmadog or Caernarfon
Car Parking:
Parking available at Caernarfon
Coach Parking:
At Victoria Docks (¼ mile from
Caernarfon station) and in Porthmadog
Souvenir Shop(s): Yes
Food & Drinks:
Full buffet available on most trains

SPECIAL INFORMATION

The Railway has been reconstructed
between Caernarfon and Porthmadog
Harbour along the track bed of the original
Welsh Highland Railway. 2011 saw the
completion of this spectacular route
passing from coast to coast through the
majestic scenery of the Snowdonia
National Park.

OPERATING INFORMATION

Opening Times: 2019 dates: Regular
services run from 30th March to 2nd
November. There is also a limited service
during the Winter plus Santa Specials on
weekends in December. Train times vary
depending on the date. Please contact the
railway for further details.
Steam Working:
Most trains are steam-hauled.
Prices: Adult £41.50 (Round trip return)
Concessions £35.90 (Round trip)
One child travels free with each adult and
additional children travel for half the fare.
Cheaper fares are available for single rides
and shorter journeys.

Detailed Directions by Car:
Take either the A487(T), the A4085 or the A4086 to Caernarfon then follow the brown tourist signs for the
Railway which is situated in St. Helens Road next to the Castle.

WELSHPOOL & LLANFAIR LIGHT RAILWAY

Address: The Station, Llanfair Caereinion, Powys SY21 0SF	**Nº of Steam Locos:** 7
	Nº of Other Locos: 5
Telephone Nº: (01938) 810441	**Nº of Members:** 2,200
Year Formed: 1959	**Annual Membership Fee:** £27.00
Location of Line: Welshpool to Llanfair Caereinion, Mid Wales	**Approx Nº of Visitors P.A.:** 26,000
	Gauge: 2 feet 6 inches
Length of Line: 8 miles	**Web site:** www.wllr.org.uk

GENERAL INFORMATION

Nearest Mainline Station: Welshpool (1 mile)
Nearest Bus Station: Welshpool (1 mile)
Car Parking: Free parking at Welshpool and Llanfair Caereinion
Coach Parking: As above
Souvenir Shop(s): Yes – at both ends of line
Food & Drinks: Yes – at Llanfair only

SPECIAL INFORMATION

The railway has the steepest gradient of any British adhesion railway (1 in 29) and reaches a summit of 603 feet.

OPERATING INFORMATION

Opening Times: 2019 dates: Every weekend and school holiday from 13th April to 3rd November. Daily from 20th July to 1st September. Every day except Mondays and Fridays from 11th May to the end of September. Santa Specials operate on 7th, 8th, 14th, 15th, 21st & 22nd December.
Trains usually run from 10.00am until 5.00pm.
Steam Working: Most trains are steam-hauled
Prices: Adult Day Rover £14.50
Senior Citizen Day Rover £13.50
Under-16s Day Rover £5.00 (Under-3s free)
(Must be accompanied)
Family Day Rover £34.00 (2 adult + 2 child)
Note: Tickets are cheaper when purchased online and in advance.

Detailed Directions by Car:
Both stations are situated alongside the A458 Shrewsbury to Dolgellau road and are clearly signposted

WEST LANCASHIRE LIGHT RAILWAY

Address: Station Road, Hesketh Bank, Nr. Preston, Lancashire PR4 6SP
Telephone Nº: (01772) 815881
Year Formed: 1967
Location of Line: On former site of Alty's Brickworks, Hesketh Bank
Length of Line: ¼ mile

Nº of Steam Locos: 9
Nº of Other Locos: 24
Nº of Members: Approximately 200
Annual Membership Fee: £20.00 Adult; £30.00 Family
Approx Nº of Visitors P.A.: 10,000
Gauge: 2 feet
Web site: www.westlancsrailway.org

GENERAL INFORMATION

Nearest Mainline Station: Preston (10 miles). Take the No. 2 bus outside the station.
Nearest Bus Station: Preston (10 miles). Take the No. 2 bus to Hesketh Bank Booths.
Car Parking: Space for 50 cars at site
Coach Parking: Space for 3 coaches at site
Souvenir Shop(s): Yes
Food & Drinks: Hot and cold drinks and snacks plus a catering van for hot fast food on Gala Days.

SPECIAL INFORMATION

The Railway is run by volunteers and there is a large collection of Industrial Narrow Gauge equipment.

OPERATING INFORMATION

Opening Times: 2019 dates: Sundays and Bank Holidays from 31st March to 3rd November. Santa Trains run on 9th, 15th, 16th, 22nd and 23rd December. Steam Gala is on 10th & 11th August and the Working Engines Gala is on 6th October. Trains run from 11.30am to 5.00pm.
Steam Working: Trains operate on Sundays and Bank Holidays from April until the end of October.
Prices: Adult £3.50   Child £2.50
              Family Tickets £9.00
              Senior Citizens £3.00
Note: Different fares apply for Gala Days and Santa Specials.

Detailed Directions by Car:
Travel by the A59 from Liverpool or Preston or by the A565 from Southport to the junction of the two roads at Tarleton. From here follow signs to Hesketh Bank. The Railway is signposted.

WINDMILL ANIMAL FARM RAILWAY

Address: Windmill Animal Farm, Red Cat Lane, Burscough L40 1UQ
Telephone Nº: (07971) 221343
Year Formed: 1997
Location of Line: Burscough, Lancashire
Length of Line: 1 mile

Nº of Steam Locos: 4
Nº of Other Locos: 10
Approx Nº of Visitors P.A.: 70,000 (with around 35,000 taking train rides)
Gauge: 15 inches
Web: www.windmillanimalfarm.co.uk

GENERAL INFORMATION

Nearest Mainline Station: Burscough (2½ miles)
Nearest Bus Station: Southport (8½ miles)
Car Parking: Available at the Farm
Coach Parking: Available at the Farm
Souvenir Shop(s): Yes
Food & Drinks: Available

SPECIAL INFORMATION

In addition to the railway, the site includes a play area and a large number of farm animals with a petting area where children can feed the animals.

OPERATING INFORMATION

Opening Times: 2019 dates: Open daily from the beginning of February until December when Santa Specials opetate. Trains run from 11.00am to 4.00pm.
Steam Working: Every weekend
Prices: Adult Admission £7.50 (Farm entrance)
Child Admission £8.50 (Farm entrance)
Senior Citizen Admission £5.50 (Farm ent.)
Family Admission £28.00 (Farm entrance)
Train Rides: Adult £2.00
Child £1.50 (Under-2s ride free)

Detailed Directions by Car:
From All Parts: Exit the M6 at Junction 27 and take the A5209 following signs for Southport. On entering Burscough follow signs for Burscough Bridge and Martin Lane. Turn left into Red Cat Lane just by Burscough Bridge train station and follow the road along for Windmill Animal Farm and the Railway.

WOODHORN NARROW GAUGE RAILWAY

Address: Woodhorn Northumberland Museum, Queen Elizabeth II Country Park, Ashington NE63 9YF **Telephone Nº**: 07930 937315 **Year Formed**: 1995 **Location of Line**: Northumberland **Length of Line**: 1,000 yards	**Nº of Steam Locos**: None **Nº of Other Locos**: 3 **Approx Nº of Visitors P.A.**: 100,000 (to the museum); 25,000 (to the railway) **Gauge**: 2 feet **Web site**: woodhornnarrowgaugerailway.weebly.com

GENERAL INFORMATION

Nearest Mainline Station: Morpeth (8 miles)
Nearest Bus Station: Ashington (1 mile)
Car Parking: Available
Coach Parking: Available
Souvenir Shop(s): Yes
Food & Drinks: Available

SPECIAL INFORMATION

The railway runs through the grounds of the Woodhorn Museum and is operated by volunteers. Wheelchair access is available on trains by request.

OPERATING INFORMATION

Opening Times: Weekends and Bank Holidays throughout the year (closed on Christmas Day and New Year's Day) and daily during School Holidays, weather permitting. Special Events are held during July. Please contact the railway for further information. Open from 10.00am to 5.00pm (4.00pm during the winter months). The last train departs at 3.30pm (at 2.30pm during the winter).
Steam Working: None
Prices: Adult Return £2.00   Adult Single £1.00
Child Return £2.00   Child Single £1.00

Detailed Directions by Car:
From All Parts: Take the A1 to the A19 at Cramlington then the A189 towards Ashington and follow the brown tourist signs for Woodhorn. (Beware of SatNav directions which may leave you on the wrong side of the local goods railway line!)

CRICH TRAMWAY VILLAGE

Address: Crich Tramway Village, Crich, Matlock, Derbyshire DE4 5DP
Telephone No: (01773) 854321
Year Formed: 1964
Location of Line: Crich
Length of Line: 1 mile

No of Steam Locos: None
No of Other Locos: 50 trams approx.
Approx No of Visitors P.A.: 100,000
Web site: www.tramway.co.uk

GENERAL INFORMATION

Nearest Mainline Station: Whatstandwell (1 mile)
Nearest Bus Station: Crich
Car Parking: Free parking available on site
Coach Parking: Free parking available on site
Souvenir Shop(s): Yes
Food & Drinks: Yes

SPECIAL INFORMATION

The admission price includes unlimited tram rides plus a host of indoor attractions.

OPERATING INFORMATION

Opening Times: 2019 dates: Daily from 16th March to 3rd November, from 10.00am. Closing times vary depending on the season. Please check the web site for further details.
Steam Working: None
Prices: Adult £17.50
Child £10.50 (ages 4 to 15)
Senior Citizen £14.00
Family Tickets £40.50
Note: Tickets purchased online and at least 24 hours in advance of the visit are 50p cheaper. Group rates for 10 or more are also available with pre-booking required.

Detailed Directions by Car:
From All Parts: The Museum is situated just of the B5035 near Crich – this is approximately 15 miles north of Derby. Exit the M1 at Junction 28 if travelling from the North or Junction 26 from the South.

GREAT ORME TRAMWAY

Address: Victoria Station, Church Walks, Llandudno LL30 2NB **Telephone Nº**: (01492) 879306 **Year Formed**: 1902 **Location of Line**: North Walk, Llandudno **Length of Line**: Approximately 1 mile	**Nº of Steam Locos**: None **Nº of Other Locos**: 4 tram units **Approx Nº of Visitors P.A.**: 200,000 **Gauge**: 3 feet 6 inches **Web site**: www.greatormetramway.co.uk

GENERAL INFORMATION

Nearest Mainline Station: Llandudno (½ mile)
Nearest Bus Station: Llandudno (½ mile)
Car Parking: Available at the Summit only
Coach Parking: Available at the Summit only
Souvenir Shop(s): Yes
Food & Drinks: Available

SPECIAL INFORMATION

The Great Orme Tramway still uses the original tramcars and is the only cable-hauled tramway still operating on Britain's public roads. The track itself climbs 679 feet to the Summit Station providing panoramic views of Llandudno Bay.

OPERATING INFORMATION

Opening Times: Daily from late March until late October with trams running from 10.00am to 6.00pm (until 5.00pm in March and October).
Steam Working: None
Prices: Adult Return £8.10
             Child Return £5.60
Note: Discounted prices for families and larger groups are also available.

Detailed Directions by Car:
From All Parts: Take the A55 Expressway to the Llandudno Junction turn-off just next to the Conwy Road Tunnel and follow the A546 through Deganwy into Llandudno. Upon reaching the seafront, turn left into North Parade adjacent to the pier then left again into Church Walks. Victoria Station is about 300 yards on the right.

SEATON TRAMWAY

Address: Riverside Depot, Harbour Road, Seaton EX12 2NQ	**No of Steam Locos**: None
Telephone No: (01297) 20375	**No of Other Locos**: 14 trams
Year Formed: 1970	**Approx No of Visitors P.A.**: 80,000+
Location of Line: Seaton to Colyton, East Devon	**Gauge**: 2 feet 9 inches
Length of Line: 3 miles	**Web site**: www.tram.co.uk

GENERAL INFO

Nearest Mainline Station: Axminster (6½ miles)
Nearest Bus Station: Seaton
Car Parking: Available on site
Coach Parking: Available on site
Souvenir Shop(s): Yes
Food & Drinks: Available at the Tramstop Cafe, Colyton and at Claudes Cafe at Seaton Station.

SPECIAL INFO

The Seaton Tramway follows a section of the former Southern Railway branch line which runs through East Devon's Axe Valley from the coastal resort of Seaton to the medieval town of Colyton. The track itself passes along the estuary of the River Axe through two nature reserves and offers excellent views of wading birds and other wildlife.

OPERATING INFO

Opening Times: 2019 dates: Trams run daily from 30th March until 3rd November then from 27th December until 5th January 2020. A special 'Polar Express Train Ride' also runs from 28th November to 24th December (excluding 2nd & 9th December). Trams run from 10.00am on most operating days.
Steam Working: Not applicable
Prices: Adult Explorer £11.00
Child Explorer £8.80
Family Explorer £35.00
Note: Different fares apply for Loyalty Card holders, return and single journeys and Special Events and Experiences.

Detailed Directions by Car:
From All Parts: Seaton Tramway is situated at the mouth of the River Axe at the side of the B3172 which can be accessed via the A358 or A3052 roads.

C000183611

LOST

NEWARK

JILLIAN CAMPBELL & MIKE COX

AMBERLEY

First published 2017

Amberley Publishing
The Hill, Stroud
Gloucestershire, GL5 4EP

www.amberley–books.com

British Library Cataloguing in Publication Data.
A catalogue record for this book is available from the British Library.

ISBN 978 1 4456 6802 4 (print)
ISBN 978 1 4456 6803 1 (ebook)

Typesetting and Origination by Amberley Publishing.
Printed in Great Britain.

Contents

	Acknowledgements	6
	Introduction	7
1.	Public Buildings	8
2.	Defences	26
3.	Domestic Buildings	31
4.	Industry	52
5.	Ecclesiastical Buildings	79
	About the Authors	93

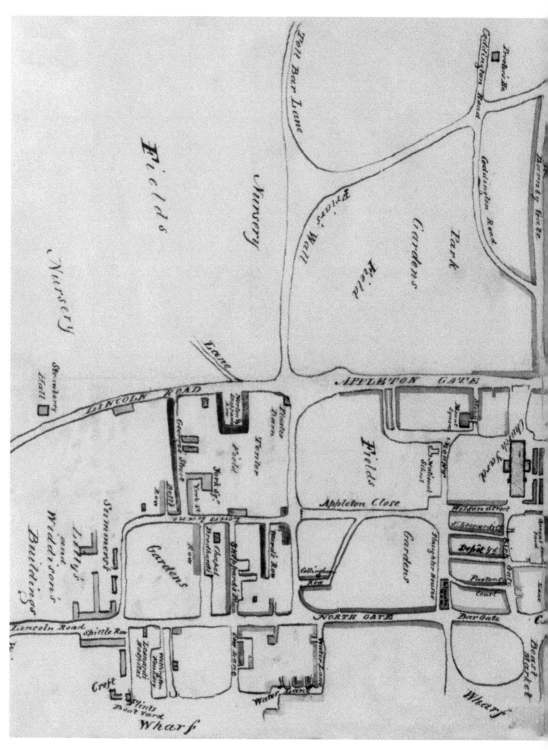

This is thought to be a political map showing coal distributions on behalf of the Duke of Newcastle, dated 1827, possibly by Richard Gamble.

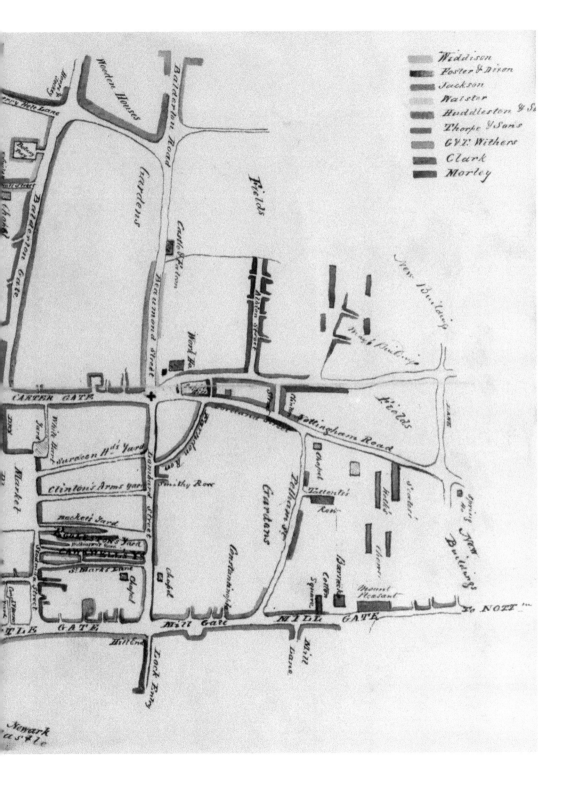

Widdison
Foster & Dixon
Jackson
Waister
Huddleston & Son
Thorpe & Sons
Gᵗ Withers
Clark
Morley

Herry & Hovey
Berry Hole Lane
Wooden Houses
Balderton Road
Balderton Gate
Gardens
Gardens
Fields
Castle & Inn
Beaumond Street
Albion Street
Ward R.
New Buildings
Mount Buildings
Fields
Lane
CARTER GATE
DRY Yard
White Hart Yard
Saracen Hᵈs Yard
Clinton's Arms yard
Lombard Street
Hackett Yard
Robertson's Yard
Smithy Row
Nottingham Road
Chapel
Gardens
Gardens
Tattenhoe's Row
Pelham Street
Constantinople
Chapel
Market
St Marks Lane
Chapel
Mill Gate
Mill Gate
MILL GATE
Fields
Stockes
Stockes
Barracks
Cotton Square
Mount Pleasant
Spring Head New Buildings
To NOTTᵐ
LITTLE GATE
Hill End
Lock Entry
Mill Lane
Newark Castle

Acknowledgements

The authors, Jill Campbell and Mike Cox, and the publishers would like to thank the following people and organisations for the help given and for the use of material in this book:

Kevin Winter and Glyn Hughes, Newark & Sherwood Museum Service, for the use of the many of the photographs shown here, and help and support in finding them in the Resource Centre Collection; and Tim Warner, Development Officer, Local Studies/ Learning, Inspire: Culture, Learning and Libraries, for permission to use some of the contents of his previous articles, and for permission to use photographs from the 'Picture the Past' collection.

Every attempt has been made to seek permission for copyright material used in this book. However, if we have inadvertently used copyright material without permission or acknowledgement we apologise and we will make the necessary correction at the first opportunity.

Introduction

In our previous two books, *Newark Through Time* and *Secret Newark*, we looked at the town through the prism of its existing buildings; however there are buildings that have been lost and leave little trace or have been altered beyond recognition, and this book will take a look at some of those. Some disappeared before the advent of photography, so it has not been possible to include illustrations of these.

Newark has been lucky in the retention of its historic fabric. Many of its pre-Civil War timber-framed buildings survive, either as complete buildings or as remnants inside later structures. The mediaeval town layout by Bishop Alexander of Lincoln has largely survived and its burgage plots still dictate development boundaries. Furthermore there was very little damage to the frontages of the town during the car park/shopping mall period at the close of the twentieth century.

The present town is largely Queen Anne and Georgian, as rebuilt after the First English Civil War (1642–46) and to accommodate the triple expansion of the town in the nineteenth century, reflecting its brewing and malting wealth.

Having said that, there have been important losses over the years, and these losses help to tell the story of the town.

1. Public Buildings

Newark has an eclectic mix of public buildings from all periods of its history.

Buildings such as the castle and the church were built by the lords of the manor but as the town grew as a market centre the town council would initiate public buildings such as the market hall and the corn exchange. Others such as the moot hall would be built by the major landholder – in the case of Newark the Duke of Newcastle.

Schools were initially charitable or religious foundations. Wealthy industrialists initially funded libraries and the hospital, but then wider local government (the county council and later the district council) would take over many areas of public life and its buildings.

The Picturedrome

Located at the corner of Barnbygate and Sherwood Avenue, the Newark Skating Rink opened in 1909 and offered skating and variety shows through the week – the skating was probably roller skating, not ice skating. After a few years the building was converted to show cine films by the London Bioscope Co. and became known as the Picturedrome.

Newark's first skating rink and Picturedrome.

It was closed in 1921 and converted to a warehouse until the 1950s, when it was demolished and replaced by housing.

Newark had three other cinemas by this time: the Kinema (now a furniture showroom) in Baldertongate, built by entrepreneur Emily Blagg, which opened its doors to the public in 1913, continuing until 1958; the Palace theatre, still a theatre and later the Savoy cinema, now a building society. All have been superseded by a modern multiscreen cinema off London Road car park.

Open-Air Swimming Pool

Newark's first swimming 'pool' was located on the arm of the Trent in Tolney Lane where the overflow from the town locks passes via a weir.

By the mid-1930s this was considered inadequate for reasons of safety and hygiene. A new Lido-style open-air pool was constructed and opened in 1934, on the Chauntry park inside the area formed by Bede House Lane, Sherwood Avenue (then called Cherry Holt Lane) and Barnbygate.

There was an Olympic size main pool with a 3-foot shallow end and an 8-foot deep end to allow for the diving boards. A water-lubricated slide was included at the halfway point of the Barnbygate side.

There was a paddling pool for small children and the water was circulated and purified via a large fountain inside the entrance area. Male and female changing cubicles were situated along the Bede House Lane boundary. The whole complex was set in

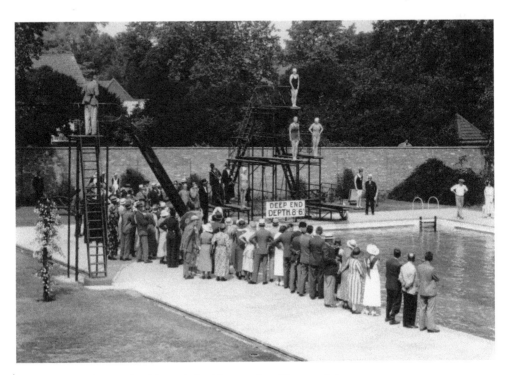

The opening of Newark's lido-style bathing pool on Sherwood Avenue, 1934.

gardens with seating for relaxation, and a cafeteria area, serving drinks and snacks – who remembers the Wagon Wheels (much larger then)?! The pool was popular and well attended with 'buses bringing in school parties from surrounding villages.

In the 1970s, new covered indoor pools were becoming popular, incorporated into the new sports centres. Newark followed the trend and with the decision to develop the Grove

Swimming area in the River Trent, off Tolney Lane.

Newark's outdoor bathing pool.

Comprehensive School at Balderton, a sports centre was developed on its campus. This included a 25-metre main pool and a training pool, with the advantage of year-round use.

The old pool site was eventually utilized as a park with the space for the main pool used as a skateboard facility.

The shallow end of the pool and the children's pool, showing the fountain.

The old bathing pool site, after closure.

Newark Bus Station

Following the nationalization of the railways after the Second World War, attempts were made to nationalize the bus companies in 1968. This project was not entirely successful and there remained a considerable number of private local companies together with the larger municipal groupings.

Newark was mainly served by the Lincolnshire Road Car Co. who ran services throughout Lincolnshire and in areas such as Newark where obvious geographical links existed.

The bus station in Newark was located behind the Robin Hood Hotel between Lombard Street and Portland Street.

A long, single-storey building behind the hotel contained (from the Portland Street end) toilets, a waiting room with art deco benches around the walls and a coal fire, a staff waiting room and an office.

The bus picking up areas were not defined, but appeared to be traditional; for example the Balderton bus would pull up next to the waiting room, the Farndon bus alongside it, meaning that passengers for Farndon had to stand in the middle of the space until a bus arrived. Lincoln buses departed from the short street linking the station with Lombard Street. They were provided with a rain canopy.

Dropping off for all services was in Portland Street or Lombard Street depending on available room. Traffic was much less in those days. Older readers may remember the 'utility' buses used on the village runs with their wooden slatted seats.

Other companies, such as GW Gash and Sons, used the station for their service to Nottingham and villages in between. Some other services used the town wharf as a pick-up/drop-off point, as today.

Behind the bus station ran Farndon Row – a row of houses running between Portland Street and Lombard Street.

Site of the old bus station on Portland Street/Lombard Street.

Newark's old bus station.

Newark's bus station, with Farndon Row in the background.

Farndon Row (from the Lombard Street end).

Public Houses

This chapter title may seem deceptive. To the ordinary man, from the early days (being a bit vague on this, as our official records only go back to the mid-eighteenth century) 'public building' meant the 'public house', where, from years past, men traditionally enjoyed a pint (or two) after working hours, before going home to an evening meal. The malting and brewing industries in Newark not only provided employment, but also the outlets for the end product!

Modern living, driving restrictions and the smoking ban have changed the functionality of the public house into somewhere that the whole family can enjoy – eating, entertainment and drinking (not necessarily the alcoholic variety).

Early inns were essential for travellers along the Great North Road, not only for Bed and Board, but also safety along the way. Water was not safe to drink, so 'small beer' (also 'small ale') was produced. Small beer is a beverage that contains very little alcohol, typically around 0.75 per cent. Sometimes unfiltered and porridge-like, it was a favoured drink in Medieval Europe as opposed to the more expensive beer with a higher alcohol content. Highwaymen and footpads were common, so the safety of a wayside inn was essential.

Newark was an important stopping-off point on the route to Edinburgh from London. The route from Grantham, however, was notoriously bad, so travellers were certainly glad of the stop at Newark for a night's stay, a change of horses and an assurance of good bed and board for the night.

Newark's Market Square boasted four coaching inns, with at least several more in the town. All have closed as inns, but the buildings are still recognisable and are named. The only loss is the Blue Bell, which stood on the site where WHSmith's now stands.

The list of lost public houses in Newark would fill a book on its own. Here are a few of them, within living memory:

The Cavalier Public House (Formerly Called 'the Angel')

The earliest known record of a public house on this site is dated 1471, where it is mentioned in a deed (Cornelius Brown's *History of Newark, Vol. II'* page twenty-six). This makes it the third-oldest known pub after the Saracen's Head (1341) and the Old White Hart (1413), both of which are in the Market Place.

The Angel was not one of Newark's coaching inns, but it was, in 1831, a pick-up point for a number of local carriers' carts. Various carriers operated on Wednesdays and Fridays from several nearby villages, and Mansfield.

In 1965, the Angel building was demolished and then rebuilt. It was renamed 'The Cavalier'. This building closed in the summer of 2001, and in the following November reported in the *Newark Advertiser* as being redeveloped as the 'Savers' health and beauty store.

Site of the old Cavalier (formerly The Angel) on the corner of Boar Lane.

The White Hind

The White Hind was on Cartergate and was also known as 'Pretty Windows'. It dates from 1796.

The White Hind public house on Cartergate.

The Broadway Inn, Bowbridge Road.

The Broadway Hotel
The Broadway Hotel was on Bowbridge Road and is now the site of a nursing home. It dates from 1939.

The Walnut Tree
The Walnut tree was Warwick's Ales public house dating from 1853–1936, stood on Lincoln Road, roughly where Lincoln Road Bridge now stands. There is still a commemorative walnut tree on the side of Northern Road. This public house was demolished to make way for Lincoln Road Bridge.

The Walnut Tree public house, Lincoln Road.

The Walnut Tree.

The walnut tree – planted on Northern Road, near Lincoln Road bridge.

Sconce Hills and Barnby Road Schools

Before the Second World War, most children, with the exception of those attending the grammar schools, attended local elementary schools in the vicinity of their homes and named after the street of their location; for example, Lovers Lane and Guildhall Street.

Most of these school buildings remain, either as primary schools (Lovers Lane) or reused and converted for other uses (Guildhall Street).

The Education Act of 1944 changed education for eleven- to fourteen-year-olds (later fifteen-year-olds) to three streams by selection at elven years of age. Approximately 20 per cent were selected as suitable for a grammar education, to prepare them for university, teaching college or the higher ranks of business training. The exact proportion depended on the number of grammar school places available. In Newark there were more places for boys than girls because there was a boys' grammar school on Southwell but no provision for girls, who therefore came to Newark. The remainder were initially sent to the new Secondary Modern Schools, whose role was to prepare them for the world of unskilled or skilled work. At ages twelve and thirteen there was a further opportunity to join the grammar stream and another selection to attend the Technical College for higher technical and secretarial skills.

Two schools provided the secondary provision in Newark: an expanded Barnby Road school and a newly built Sconce Hills School.

Following the Second World War, the Cold War between the Warsaw Pact nations and NATO began and there was a real fear that should this war in Europe become 'hot', there would be widespread civilian casualties. Sconce Hills School was therefore built to allow it to be rapidly converted to a hospital should it be needed. It was a single-storey building with wide corridors with rooms coming off of them, whereas most school buildings were built around a central assembly hall with rooms off that.

In 1974, Nottinghamshire became fully comprehensive for secondary education. Because of the buildings available, Newark had an unusual system of lower (eleven to fourteen) and upper (fifteen to sixteen or eighteen). The two grammar schools became the upper schools and Sconce Hills and Barnby Road the lower schools, called High Schools.

The schools were operated as pairs. Barnby Road, now called Magdalene High, and Thomas Magnus School were paired and Sconce Hills were paired with Lilley and Stone School. The two head teachers, who lived in town but did not wish to live in their own school's catchment area, decided the catchments of the two High Schools; they drew a complex line through the town.

Owing to government changes in the funding of schools, the two-school system became unsustainable and it was decided to have two large comprehensives to serve the town. Because the old grammar schools had covenanted sites it was decided to extend those and demolish the High Schools. In 2000, the new schools were ready and all of Sconce Hills School and all of Barnby Road (Magdalene) School, with the exception of a small original building, were demolished and replaced by housing.

Albert Street Barracks

Albert Street Barracks was a substantial building complex surrounded by a wall and located in the corner formed by Albert Street and Boundary Road.

The Sherwood Rangers (originally the Sherwood Foresters Militia) was a cavalry regiment, but during the First World War converted to cycles and later to light tanks or scout cars.

The buildings were demolished in 1974 and replaced by private housing and a fire station.

The old barracks site, after closure.

Newark Barracks, from Boundary Road.

The rear of Newark Barracks.

The barracks being
demolished.

View of the barracks.

The barracks from Albert Street.

The barracks from Hawton Road.

Newark's First Theatre

This building, once thought to be Newark's first real purpose-built theatre, was built in 1773 on Middlegate, on a site now occupied partly by Millets store, and the Covered-in Market backing onto Newark Town Hall.

Work began on the theatre in November 1772 and the final cost was £360 3s 2d – this price included the cost of demolishing the previous buildings on the site. A sketch plan shows its location between the Duke of Cumberland public house and the butchers' shambles, which stood where the Covered-in Market now stands.

The first recorded play was staged in June 1773, when Mr Whitely's Company of Comedians announced that they would perform for six nights in Newark, on their way to Nottingham Races.

The building was then leased to the Lincoln Circuit Theatre Co., who toured theatres in Lincoln, Boston and Grantham. An annual season in Newark lasted between six to eight weeks in November and December. At other times the building was let for other purposes.

In 1803, the building was enlarged and improved upon. The local papers quoted 'The design and execution of the theatre cannot be too highly spoken of. It is truly elegant, and Newark can boast one of the handsomest Provincial Theatres in the kingdom.'

Many famous actors and personalities of the day during its 100-year history trod its boards. Its most noted local person however was Thomas William Robertson (1829–71), who became one of the most celebrated playwrights of late Victorian England. Coming from a family connected to the theatre, he flourished and later went on to become famous in London with his writings and plays. Eldest son of William Robertson

Site of Newark's first theatre (on the left).

Site of Newark's first theatre, Middlegate.

(a provincial actor and manager), he was born in Newark's theatre. A pioneer of what is now modern stage management, he showed how to give life and variety to scenes.

Diminishing audiences in the late 1830s led to its closure. By 1850 the building had been sold and converted to a house, shop and workshops. By 1884 it was partly demolished, and the construction of the Covered-in market commenced. Traces of the theatre may be identified in the present Millets frontage on Middlegate, in the three first-floor windows, and possibly its hipped roof.

Woolworth's

F. W. Woolworth & Co. first came to Newark in 1932. It started life in America, by Frank Winfield Woolworth, who was one of the original pioneers of the 'five-and-dime' stores. It opened in New York in 1878 as 'Woolworth's Great Five Cent Store'. After initial failure, the second successful store opened in Pennsylvania.

Newark's Store opened to great acclaim and celebration, and was extremely successful. However, declining sales in America and elsewhere due to increased competition led to stores closing. Newark's store closed in 1984.

Briefly resurfacing on Northgate as 'Woolies', the chain went out of business in 1997.

I think many of us remember the sawdust on the wooden floor in the original shop, and bemoan the demise of the pick 'n' mix!

F. W. Woolworth & Co., Stodman Street.

2. Defences

Newark began life as an Anglo-Saxon burgh or fortified town in the ninth century AD. The defended perimeter grew in area over the centuries to reach the large fortified town of the Civil War third siege. Much of this defensive structure is still discernible around the town and can be explored using the information systems available at the National Civil War Centre. Some important elements however have been lost in the later development of the town.

The town holds the finest surviving examples of Civil War siege works in England, and several buildings in the town that had connections with the Civil War can still be seen.

Its name 'Key to the North' epitomised Newark's strategic importance – its control of the crossing of the Great North Road with the Roman Fosse Way and the River Trent. It was important for King Charles to keep open his routes to his headquarters in Oxford.

In the 1640s, England was in turmoil – the relations between king and Parliament had broken down, and all of England had to choose which side to champion. Because the Crown owned much of the land around Newark, and Charles was a regular visitor, Newark supported the king and played a nationally strategic role in events. Charles came to Newark in July 1642 to reaffirm the town's allegiance and assemble troops. Following his raising of his standard at Nottingham in August of that year, England was cast into a bloody and interminable war that was to last four years and culminate in the king's demise and the almost ruination of the town.

Newark withstood three Sieges. The first in February 1643 lasted only two days, when Newark's governor, Sir John Henderson, successfully repulsed an attack led by Major General Thomas Ballard, who, descending on the town from Beacon Hill, realised the town's defences were too strong. Henderson's first act as governor had been to order all townsfolk and the soldiers of the garrison to begin building a new defensive circuit around the town, beyond the medieval walls.

The second siege came a year later, and lasted three weeks. In the intervening year, Queen Henrietta Maria came to Newark in June 1643, and by that time there were approximately 2,000 troops in the town. Sir Richard Byron was now a governor – an able and capable Royalist commander. By February 1644 Newark was once again under siege. Sir John Meldrum surrounded the town with a 7,000-strong army and attacked with eleven cannons and two mortars. It was during this attack that Newark's parish church spire was hit – the hole is still visible to this day. The mayor of Newark, Alderman Hercules Clay, had his home demolished. Meldrum's troops continued to bombard the town and gain ground in the vicinity – Muskham Bridge and the 'Island' fell into Parliamentary hands. Help was at hand, however, when the region's Royalist commander, Lord Loughborough, appealed to King Charles' nephew and cavalry commander, Prince Rupert of the Rhine, for help. Espying Meldrum's headquarters at Exeter House (near the Spital on Northgate) he, together with 6,400 of his own troops and those of Lord Loughborough's, swept down from Beacon Hill and quickly drove the Parliamentarian ranks from the town. Muskham Fort and the Island were soon recaptured. The haul of armaments included ammunition and around 3,000 muskets. Among the cannon was a great 32-pounder known as 'Sweet Lips' (purportedly named after a lady of ill-repute from Hull!).

Despite this victory, Lord Byron knew that Newark's defences were precarious. He ordered further strengthening of the earthworks, namely, in Millgate (to protect the powder mills) and the construction of the King's Sconce (destroyed in around 1887) and Queen's Sconce (SK791531), which remains today as one of the best-preserved of Newark's Civil War earthworks.

The date 26 November 1645 saw Newark's third and longest siege. Sir Richard Willys had been governor since late 1644, but due to increasing Royalist defeats around the country, culminating in the king's defeat at Naseby in 1645, Newark found itself isolated as a Royalist town surrounded by Parliamentary control. This only strengthened the town's resolve. In October 1645, the king paid his last visit to the town. A desperate king argued with his nephew, Prince Rupert (the latter having come to Newark to explain his surrender of Bristol), and both Rupert and Willys left Newark, Willys having been accused of misappropriating vital military funds.

It was left to Lord John Belasyse to command Newark through its last and most eventful siege of the Civil War. Colonel General Sydenham Poyntz and Colonel Rossiter encircled the town and slowly joined the ring of Parliamentarian strongholds that went from Farndon to Winthorpe. The Scots army, under the command of General Alexander Leslie, 1st Earl Leven, took control of the Island to the north of the town.

Belasyse prepared the town for a long siege. He realised there was little hope. He provisioned the town as best he could and to overcome the shortage of money established a mint in the castle, where the distinctive Newark Siege Pieces (produced from donated silverware) were stamped. Despite strengthening the town's ramparts, by March 1646, some 7,000 Scots and 9,000 English troops were surrounding the town. Poyntz determined the town should at last surrender, not only by battering the defences, but also by starving the inhabitants. A contemporary account states that 'Newark became a miserable, stinking infected town where sickness was rife.'

Meanwhile, at Oxford, King Charles was considering how best to surrender. He resolved to hand himself over to the Scots army camped near Newark. Belasyse wrote to him asking what he should do.

The King replied:

Belasyse, such is the condition of affaires att this present that I can give you no hope att all of relief…wherefore the best for my service will be that you conclude upon them with all expedition, the cheefe reason being that according to my dessigne I am necessitated to march with the Scotch army this day northwards, but cannot move till this agreement be consented to by you. I am heartily sorry that my business stands so as that I must impose such condisions upon you.

Charles R.

The town surrendered. The Castle was dismantled – and Newark's war was over

The Kings' Sconce

Following the second siege of Newark in the English Civil War, the defenders realised that the Parliamentary army would try again to capture the town. To counter this threat, extensive earthworks were constructed in and around the town. An inner ditch and rampart was dug along Sleaford Road, along the Friary Road and then towards Victoria Street. Part of this earthwork is still apparent in the Friary gardens.

A plan drawing of King's Sconce on Northgate.

In addition, in order to protect the approaches to the town from the south west and north east along the Fosse Way, two large sconces were constructed. The southern sconce, called the Queen's Sconce, can be seen in the park that bears its name. The other similar sconce, called the King's Sconce, lay to the north-east of the town, where

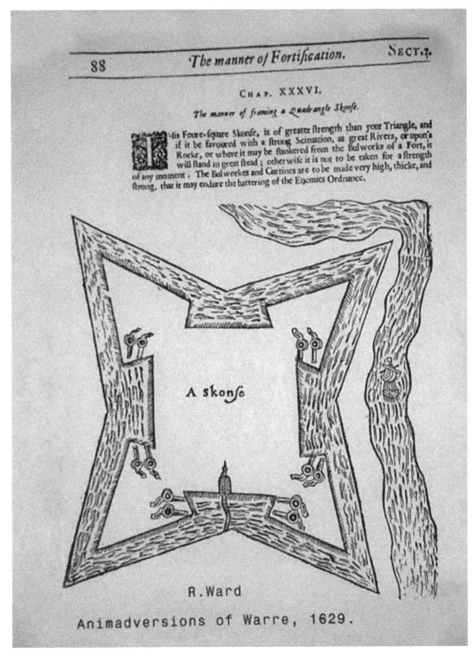

A drawing of a 'Skonse'.

a retail park now stands. This sconce was demolished to make way for the construction of the Great Northern Railway in 1856.

The Sconce was a Dutch development. Being built of earth it is not as vulnerable to cannon fire as a stone wall. The hornwork, which is the basis of the sconce, channels the attackers into an area where they are exposed to fire from several sides. A hornwork can be placed along a linear defensive ditch and a rampart or groups of four or more, to create a sconce.

Town Wall

The early Saxon town existed in the area bounded by the river, Kirk Gate, Middlegate and Stodman Street. Later, in the medieval period, the town developed a 'wall', lying inside the area bounded by Slaughterhouse Lane / Mount Lane/ Appletongate / Carter Gate, and Lombard Street. This was a ditch and vallum type of defence – i.e., a deep dry ditch where the excavated earth is thrown inwards to provide a base for a wooden palisade or perhaps a stone wall. Tantalising glimpses of this defence are to be seen around the town, together with some small pieces of wall along its line, built of the local oolitic limestone.

As medieval defences of this type became obsolete, houses were built against the outside of the wall, creating the streets named above.

Possible outline of the town wall.

3. Domestic Buildings

The oldest Newark domestic buildings are the timber-framed houses, which date from the middle of the fourteenth century. These houses would have been originally thatched using local reed from the river or barley straw.

During the period following the English Civil War, there was an increased use of the local bricks made from clay mined from the area of Beacon Hill and Coddington. Roofing materials were probably clay pantiles, but given the river and later rail transport links, slate became the dominant material. These bricks give the town its distinctive red-brick appearance and many of these still stand. In some cases, the bricks are used decoratively with the headers in a lighter colour than the stretchers, giving a mottled appearance to the wall. This would be purely for appearance to display wealth.

Newark's Anglo-Saxon origins have produced a layout of 'burgage plots' – long plots stretching back from the street with a narrow frontage of one rod or perch (approximately 5 metres long). With the threefold increase in population in the nineteenth century, these plots were used to create back-to-back houses within yards.

Much of this structure was demolished in the 1960s and the populations moved to the new Hawtonville estate. This, incidentally, was done yard by yard so that neighbours ended up living in the same groupings on the new estate.

In the latter part of the nineteenth and early twentieth centuries, the town expanded from its earlier limits and a 'new town' area was developed between London Road and Barnbygate, consisting of terraced houses of various designs – some very plain, others with bay windows. These terraces consist of much larger houses than those in the town and are often larger than the later semi-detached houses. Each street had a shop, church/chapel or public house at its end.

More substantial houses for the middle and upper classes were built on or around London Road.

Some of these domestic buildings, indeed whole streets, have vanished, and are described below.

Chauntry House

Chauntry House and its park was originally the site of lands of a medieval chauntry.

In the medieval church, the doctrine of Purgatory was of great importance. It is 'an intermediate state after physical death in which some of those ultimately destined for heaven must first undergo purification, so as to achieve the holiness necessary to enter the joy of heaven'.

The front of Chauntry House, Appletongate.

The rear of Chauntry House.

Chauntry House gardens.

The rear of Chauntry House gardens.

THE CHAUNTRY
NEWARK – UPON – TRENT.

CATALOGUE
OF THE VALUABLE CONTENTS
TO BE SOLD BY AUCTION.

Charles Jno. Ridge,
AUCTIONEER.

Auction & Valuation Offices,
25, MARKET PLACE, NEWARK.

Sale catalogue of contents at Chauntry House.

Contents of Chauntry House.

Imagined sketch of an original Chauntry House.

This doctrine led to practices such as the selling of indulgences, which would ease the soul's passage through Purgatory. Another practice was to leave money in a will to provide for a priest to say masses for the soul of the departed, with the same end in mind.

In a wealthy town such as Newark with its rich wool merchants, several of these would be set up over the period. It is thought as many as nineteen existed in Newark. Revd F. J. Dimock says, 'We might search through all England, and should find few indeed, if any, parish churches which could boast such an array of Chantries as Newark possessed in the fourteenth and fifteenth centuries.'

During the Wars of the Roses, Newark was the scene of warlike demonstrations. Edward IV passed through the town on his way to combat the wearers of the Red Rose gathered at Doncaster. His Majesty was 'worshipfully accompanied' to the castle, and there marched through the streets of Newark so many 'goodly men well arrayed that it was said the like had not been seen in England before'.

The priests in question sang their masses in the parish church of St Mary Magdalene and were housed in a building founded by Alice Fleming, widow of a wool merchant, rather like a small monastery within the town. This was located in the area between the Friary grounds and Coddington Lane (now Bedehouse Lane).

An excerpt from one such will illustrates this point: 'the said chauntry is no parish church', but within the parish church of Newark 'it has no mansion, but a chamber in the common house amongst other of the brethren'.

Henry VIII dissolved most of the large monasteries, but it was his son, Edward VI, who finished the job, with dissolution and confiscation of the chantries. During the reign of Elizabeth I, the Protestant church reformed its thinking and removed these doctrines and practices.

The land acquired from these monasteries and chauntries was sold off to wealthy merchants and the Newark Chauntry was demolished in the eighteenth century to be replaced by the impressive Queen Anne-style house illustrated.

This house, with its deer park, was ultimately lived in by Revd Joseph Sikes, but in the early twentieth century was acquired by Mrs Emily Blagg, a local industrialist who sold off the contents and demolished the house to build a theatre. The majority of the park is now the campus of Newark College. The lodge to the property originally stood at the corner of Sherwood Avenue and Barnbygate. It was demolished prior to the building of Newark's outdoor swimming pool.

Parsons Mount Vicarage

Parsons Mount is the area of land formerly used as the town burial ground in the north-east corner of the medieval town wall north of the church of St Mary Magdalene.

Once marking the northern boundary of Newark in medieval times, access today is via Mount Lane, off Appletongate. A stout, defensive wall ran along this route, approximately along Slaughterhouse Lane along to Northgate.

'The Mount' (or Mound) is believed to get its name from a large earthen platform situated behind this medieval wall, which was probably used as a lookout point across the open country to the north. A former name was 'Parson's Mound', and it was mentioned in William Dickinson's book *History and Antiquities of Newark*, published in 1815, as being able to be seen at the time of his writing (around 1806).

Cornelius Brown, in his history of the town, says that all traces of the Mound were finally dismantled in the 1820s, when the Mount School was built.

This plot of land was also occupied by the early vicarage, and the small door in the north transept of the chancel, giving access to the vicar can, still be seen. This vicarage

North door of Newark Parish Church.

The old grammar school frontage on Appletongate.

was demolished and replaced by the fine Queen Anne house across Appletongate directly east of the church.

The building is not entirely lost as the then headmaster of the Magnus Grammar School, a Mr Wittenoon, acquired the materials to construct an extension to the school to accommodate extra paying pupils from outside the town.

This building was erected close up and in front of the Tudor School building, obscuring most of it from the street view.

Ironmongers Row – Forgotten Area of Newark

It is hard to envisage that in this area around the south side of the parish church of St Mary Magdalene, with its peaceful seating, wide paving and spaciousness, prior to 1892 there was a built-up area comprising two rows of buildings pressed up to the church. Known as Ironmonger's Row, the area was made up of a tallow chandlery, a slaughterhouse, stables and a fish and rabbit shop, owned by George Winn. It is said that in warm weather the church congregation had to move to the other side of the church as the smell was so overpowering.

On the evening of 23 December 1891, with Christmas preparations in full swing, a disastrous fire broke out in the premises of James Knight, draper, in the Market Place. The windows were decorated for Christmas, and when the Knight's shop boy lit the gas lamps

Ironmongers' Row – before the fire.

to illuminate them, some caught fire. The fire spread rapidly, threatening the whole block of buildings not only on the Market Place, but the whole of Ironmonger's Lane behind it.

In Wilkinson's tallow chandlery there were large stores of candles, and it was feared that if these caught fire, the church itself would be in danger. In the nick of time the fire engine from Warwick's Brewery arrived on the scene and poured water over the rear of the burning buildings, thus halting the progress of the flames.

The town's fire brigade tackled the blaze from the Market Place in front. Together the two firefighting groups succeeded in bringing the fire under control. The church was saved, but it is estimated that damage amounting to around £5,000 was caused to shops along the Market Place.

Almost immediately a public subscription was set up to buy the ramshackle buildings of Ironmonger Lane and demolish them to provide a firebreak between the Market Place and the church. The whole of the area was eventually bought for £1,850 and finally demolished in 1892.

The main area remained clear until 1934 when Burton's Tailors and Gent's Outfitters built their store, at the end fronting the Market Place.

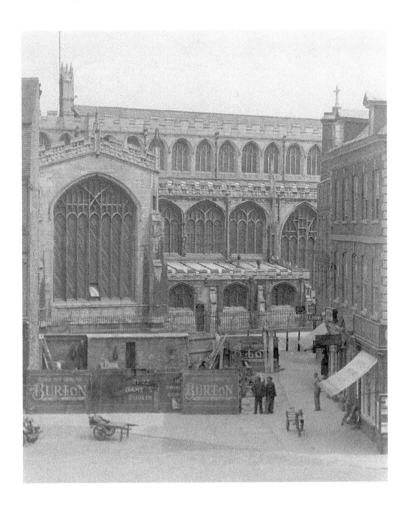

Burton's shop site – under construction.

A view of Church Walk.

Covell's Fish & Game Shop

On 20 January 1954, the *Newark Advertiser* reported that the demolition of this sixteenth-century timber-framed building at the corner of Stodman Street and Middlegate had begun the previous weekend. By 19 January only the last traces remained of the mud-packed wattle roof and the interior walls were well under way of disappearing forever.

This building, remembered by many Newark people, was last used as two shops (shown here is Covell's Fish & Game Shop) and was of the same date as the Governor's House (mid-fifteenth century to early sixteenth century), but represented a more simpler, basic type of half-timbered property.

Officially it was on the list for preservation, but had been allowed to lapse into a state beyond repair and was becoming dangerous. Upon its disappearance, Newark lost one of the last vestiges of what the town resembled during the English Civil War period of the seventeenth century. The corner has now been extended over this area.

Covell's Game shop, the corner of
Middlegate and Stodman Street.

Covell's shop, Stodman Street.

Covell's shop after being demolished.

Dutch Houses, Millgate

'Dutch' or Flemish gables were common in Germany and Holland in the fifteenth and sixteenth centuries. They consisted of curved side walls with a pediment at the top and could be incorporated into a house frontage or as a decorative addition to the building.

They started to appear in England in the sixteenth century, due to trade and the migration of people from the Low Countries. East Anglia has a strong tradition of Dutch Gables. Other examples in Newark were also seen in the Bishop Warburton's House on Cartergate – long since demolished.

The weak point of this style of building was at the joint between the gable and the outer wall. This was the undoing of this Millgate complex of houses.

Although there is no actual proof, the house was possibly occupied by the Milnes family from the late seventeenth century to the mid-eighteenth century.

By 1871 the house was in multi-occupancy by Charles Staniland, a master builder; Betsey Edmundson, a retired brazier and Mary Hardy, a seamstress. By the late nineteenth century, eleven people were listed as living in the complex of houses, and the decline had set in, continuing until 1965. The gables had become detached, and although listed Grade II in 1962, they were neglected. Newark Corporation stepped in and erected scaffolding to act as a temporary support for the building, but declined to purchase it because of the enormous cost. The owner stated that he wished to demolish, and despite public opposition, this course of action occurred.

The watercolour illustration of the Newark Dutch Houses is by the artist Elliot Ettwell and can be seen at the Resource Centre.

'Dutch houses' on Millgate.

A watercolour of the Dutch houses on Millgate by Elliot Ettwell.

Regent Street and Union Terrace

Since the 1960s, wide redevelopment and urban clearances have accounted for the destruction of many fine old corners of historic Newark. Few of these vanished treasures, however, could compete for originality with the former terrace of early nineteenth-century housing known as Regent Street, situated between Albert Street and Portland Street, together with Union Terrace, off Victoria Street.

Although demolished in 1967, the site of Regent Street may still be easily recognised today. And although designated a street, in literal terms at least, Regent Street cannot be considered a street at all. It possessed no road and was really nothing more than a row of houses (albeit of a rather superior kind) with gardens and a walkway at the front and a passageway behind.

The period of the Regency in English history – when because of George III's illness, George, Prince of Wales, acted as Prince Regent – lasted from 1811 to 1820. Regent Street in Newark, however, is of slightly later date with construction having begun in 1828. It was the work of a local man, William Kelk, who, during the early years of the nineteenth century rose to become one of Newark's most influential citizens.

Born in 1800, Kelk's family lived on Portland Street, where his father, also called William, had workshops for his joinery and cabinetmaking business. We do not know the circumstances that led the young William into the building trade, nor how he succeeded

Regent Street – view from Albert Street.

Regent Street detail.

A balcony in Regent Street.

in amassing the necessary funds to become such a successful property developer. Although Regent Street may be considered his single most impressive development in the town, Kelk was also responsible for at least three other large-scale schemes. Off King Street, for instance, he was responsible for an extensive development of three blocks of back-to-back workers' houses originally named Kelk's Buildings (subsequently renamed Queen Street Square and Kings Arms Yard, and now all demolished).

Fronting onto Victoria Street, meanwhile, he built a further group of three houses – most distinguished – known as Union Terrace, featuring elegantly carved lintels, a delicate cast-iron balcony, and projecting bowed pavilions at either end (pictured here).

Behind this terrace he built ten more houses, which became known as Union Row. (Union Terrace and Union Row have now also been demolished – in 1967 and 1972, respectively – with the site now being partially occupied by the Bishop Alexander Court sheltered housing complex.)

While William Kelk's authorship of these projects is well documented, we know frustratingly little about other aspects of his life in the town. Trade directories show that by 1822 he was operating as a builder with premises on Portland Street. By 1830 his business address was given as Stodman Street.

The town's electoral register for 1832, meanwhile, records him as living in Regent Street, although by 1834 his home address is given as Union Terrace. His name appears once again in the electoral register for 1836, although in the copy of this document held at Newark Library his entry has been crossed out and a note added to the effect that he had, by that time, left the town.

Union Terrace on Victoria Street.

A detail from Union Terrace.

Attempts to trace Kelk's movements after his departure from Newark have so far proved fruitless.

While living in Newark, however, he certainly seems to have moved within the best circles, becoming particularly involved in town politics – in those days very much a rich man's game.

In 1829, we find Kelk as chairman of the Blue Independent Committee proposing Mr Serjeant Wilde as parliamentary candidate for Newark, and in 1832, when W. E. Gladstone was first elected as MP for the town, Kelk is recorded as presenting some very searching questions on behalf of the Blues as to Gladstone's father's involvement with the slave trade.

It was around this same time, of course, that Kelk was also creating his most lasting mark upon the town in the form of his housing developments at Union Row, Union Terrace and Regent Street. Regent Street appears to have marked the midpoint in Kelk's building around Newark being commenced in 1828 when he purchased 1,697 square yards of land in the area and immediately erected seven houses upon it. Two years later (after further purchase of land) he built another ten houses, naming the entire development Regent Street.

Although many people may remember Regent Street towards the end of its life as being rather rundown and neglected, when first built, its imposing size and fine architectural detailing – notably its carved-stone lintels and quoin stones – marked it out as a noteworthy addition to the town. The centre house, taller than the rest with an impressive pediment and imposing internal stone staircase, was built for Kelk himself and known as Regent House, and by the 1880s it had been divided into two dwellings. Kelk lived there for only a few short years before his removal to Union Terrace and subsequent departure from the town.

Tenter Buildings and Elgin Place

The site of Tenter buildings, off Appletongate.

Tenter buildings and Elgin Place.

Tenter buildings and Elgin Place.

Due to the Industrial Revolution, the population of towns increased, giving rise to a number of yards and squares to house the growing number of inhabitants. Newark was no exception, and Tenter Buildings and Elgin place, off Appletongate, was one of the largest areas. A common practice was to name yards after trades that were to be found there, such as Tenter Buildings, which took its name from the word 'tenterhooks', used for the drying of manufactured cloth. Consisting, as it did, of many back-to-back dwellings, this complex has now disappeared except for one house.

Overall, Newark has references to some 700 different yards, with around 1,800 different names among them. A good many can no longer be found on the ground today, as the yard has long been absorbed into the street of which it formed a part. Some have bricked-in entrances, some no longer bear nameplates and a number have been privatised and sealed-off by means of gates across the archway. It should not be assumed, though, that every archway was the access to a yard or court, as the rounded arch structure dates back to Norman times, and the pointed arch to later medieval Gothic architecture, some of which remains.

Portland Street Houses

This picture was taken looking south along Portland Street close to its junction with Lombard Street and London Road. The houses were soon to be demolished and a notice on them states that the site is for sale. The site has been redeveloped and is occupied by the flats of Portland Court. The date 1937 is significant as it marked the early stages of Newark's first wave of slum clearances. Their progress was interrupted

Houses on Portland Street.

by the Second World War and resumed in earnest in the 1950s. On the left of the picture is the entrance to a narrow thoroughfare called Pepper Hill. Situated just opposite Hole's Castle Brewery, this small lane connected Portland Street with Albert Street. One former resident of Newark remembers how the houses here were entered through a front door and down two steps into the parlour. Today, the area between Pepper Hill and the junction of Portland Street and Albert Street has been laid out as a small garden.

Wilson Street

Dr Bernard Wilson was a son of a Newark mercer who showed prodigious talent, obtaining a place at Trinity College where he was able to advance himself socially by making friends with, among others, the son and heir of the Duke of Newcastle. At this time his father had acquired the old friary buildings, which he was able to let out as apartments. One of the occupants was a wealthy young lady called Miss Radford, and Bernard succeeded in securing her affections. Also at this time the vicarage of Newark became available and Bernard acquired this post through his friendship with the patron, the Duke of Newcastle.

Wilson was a popular vicar and a good preacher and published a translation of discourses by eminent French academicians that he dedicated to Sir George Markham, one of the town's MPs. As a reward, George gave Bernard management of large estates in Lincolnshire and recommended him as a husband to Miss Ogle, daughter of an Irish gentleman.

Although living with Miss Radford, he also paid his addresses to a Lady Finch and a Miss Davis. Lady Finch rejected him but Miss Davis sued for breach of promise and was awarded £7,000. He was also involved in lawsuits with the Ogle family that resulted in an out-of-court settlement of £30,000. He then married Miss Radford.

His next move was to build up his influence in local politics, which led to a fallout with his patron, the Duke of Newcastle. In order to gain political status in the town he distributed gifts, and airing land at the north side of the church, built Wilson Street. The purpose of building the properties was to let them to the town's people, who would then be coerced to vote for him – the normal practice at the time.

The street was a double row of Palladian terraces facing one another across the rather narrow street. Each side had three pavilions: one at each end and one central one. The pavilions were three stories and would have been substantial houses at the time. The street gradually became rundown and during the 1970s the east side was partly demolished with the exception of the end pavilions, opening up the area to the churchyard and increasing the light entering the opposite properties.

Dr Wilson died in 1772 and it is said that £5,000 worth of gold guineas were found in various parts of his house.

View of both sides of Wilson Street.

4. Industry

Newark's earliest 'industry' was sheep farming. Initially, this was very much the domain of the monasteries and other similar groups. Evidence of the wealth that this generated in the town is the church of St Mary Magdalene, which is very much a 'wool church' in the manner of those in East Anglia.

With the Reformation and the destruction of monastic power in the sixteenth century, the rich fertile lands along the Trent Valley began to grow barley. This is the raw material of beer. Small breweries and maltings began in the town using the good artesian water available. Eventually, the industry came to be dominated by two large breweries and the malting firm of Gilstrap and Earp (Later ABM). As farming mechanized in the nineteenth century, workers from the countryside moved into towns where agricultural machinery manufactories were established together with smock making and basket working.

In 1899, two major manufacturers moved into the town Ransome's, making woodworking and other farming machinery, and James Simpson, a pump manufacturer from London.

This strong industrial position continued until the second half of the twentieth century, after which it entered a gradual decline until the town had no dominant industry.

Newark Gas Works

Town gas or coal gas is made by burning coal in a controlled environment so that the resultant gas can be drawn off for storage. It has a distinctive smell from its constituents, a mixture consisting primarily of carbon monoxide (CO), hydrogen (H_2), carbon dioxide (CO_2), methane (CH_4), and water vapour (H_2O), unlike its replacement North Sea gas, which has to have a smell added for domestic use. The process also produces useful by-products of tar and coke, used for steel making and as a cheaper domestic fuel.

Gas House Lane records the location of the town's former gasworks. The present name for the street, Parker Street, commemorates the man who was a prime mover in bringing gas to the town.

In 1832, William Parker was Mayor of Newark and in July of that year he presided over a meeting at the Clinton Arms Hotel at which it was decided to establish a Gas Light and Coke Company. The foundation stone for the town gasworks (originally at the northern end of Whitfield Street) was laid by William Parker on 23 August 1832, and by the end of the year selected parts of the town were benefiting from supplies

Proposed gasworks.

of locally manufactured coal gas. The first area to be lit was Church Walk, where the original lamps were in use until the end of the twentieth century. The original standards are retained with modern electric lights.

The company also accepted a contract from the town council to provide street lighting, replacing the feeble oil lamps that had hitherto been erected around the town.

As demand for gas grew, the original works on Whitfield Street became unable to cope, and in 1883 the company acquired a new site on Barnbygate where it built a greatly enlarged facility. The original works were built at a cost of £5,000.

It was at this time that Gas House Lane came into being, retaining that name until 1903 when it was officially renamed Parker Street in honour of Mayor William Parker.

The works had a dedicated railway siding and associated coal yard from the northern line situated east of Vine Street.

The first balance sheet showed the wages paid for the year as £83 and the coal purchased amounted to £269.

The 1885 OS map shows five storage containers (gasometers) of various sizes, although these were to be replaced by one large one. By the beginning of the twentieth century most of the town and some surrounding villages were served by the gasworks.

Gas was originally used for lighting purposes and was charged at so much per burner, the price varying according to the height of the flame. Some of the regulations in the early days were curious:

'For wilfully wasting or improperly using any gas – a fine of £10.'
'Accidentally wasting any gas or keeping lights burning for a longer time than contracted for – such sum as a Justice shall award.'

The use of gas expanded for cooking purposes and for fires – a considerable improvement from the old arrangements with solid fuel. Older residents will remember the smell, which pervaded this part of the town. The works had its own sidings to bring coal to the site. A by-product of gas manufacture from coal was the production of coke, a valuable and less expensive heating source for much of the population.

A steady growth in sales continued until the outbreak of the Second World War, when the usefulness of gas proved even greater, and sales increased by 25 per cent.

As the twentieth century moved on, gas lighting and some cooking was replaced by electricity and demand decreased, although coke was much in demand during the Second World War and in the exceptional winter of 1947.

The end of coal gas was brought on by the development of North Sea gas in the 1970s. This saw the demolition of the works and its replacement by a distribution complex. After the removal of the gasometer the vacant space was utilized for retail warehousing, although this has recently been replaced by a housing development.

Staythorpe Power Stations

Just prior to the Second World War the regional electricity grids were being united to make a national grid. With the nationalization plans of the post-war government, and the expected increase in domestic use, more generating capacity was required and plans were drawn up for new generating stations on major rivers and estuaries. As the River Trent is one of the country's major rivers and runs through one of its major coalfields, it was an obvious choice.

Construction began on the original Staythorpe A Power Station in July 1946, on a site just upstream where the two branches of the Trent divide at Averham Weir. The first unit commenced operation in March 1950. The coal-fired power station consisted of six power generation units, each providing a 60,000 kW output – enough to supply 200,000 homes. The units were housed in an attractive sandstone-coloured brick

Staythorpe power station under construction.

Staythorpe power station under floodlight.

building in a pre-war style, with three bays and chimneys 425 feet high, each with two generating sets. Staythorpe A received an average weekly supply of 26,000 tons from the local coal mines, making it a driving force in the local economy. All coal deliveries were by train from the adjacent line from Newark to Nottingham.

At the same time, the local countryside was transformed by the lines of high-voltage pylons radiating out from its substation into the surrounding rural landscape.

Staythorpe B, another coal plant, was officially opened on 4 May 1962, with the aim of providing an assured local market for the rapidly expanding East Midlands coalfield, and supplying cheap electricity for transmission to power-short areas of the country. The station housed £40,000,000 worth of machinery, including three generating units each with a 120,000 kW capacity.

By the time of the building of Staythorpe B Station, ideas on industrial architecture had moved on to embrace a more functional style and the building was little more than a box to protect its machinery and workers from the weather and with a single chimney.

At the time of its opening, Staythorpe B was one of the most modern and efficient coal-fired power stations anywhere in the country, far outstripping its sister station next door. In order to prevent the cooling water from overheating the river, natural draft wet cooling hyperboloid towers were added. Whereas Staythorpe A used six 60-mW turbines to achieve the required 350 mW output, Staythorpe B could produce the same power with just three.

As efficiencies increased, with the coming of nuclear power and the decline of the local coalfields, the A and B stations were decommissioned in 1983 and 1994 and demolished to be replaced by the current gas-fired station generating 1,650 mW of electricity. Only the water inlet house from the river survives from the original A station.

Worthington Simpson Erecting Shop

The Worthington Simpson erecting shop stood out above the rest of the plant and above the low-lying land of the Balderton fens like a tall aircraft hangar. The building, dating from 1911, was only two-thirds of its original intended length.

James Simpson and Co. Ltd was an engineering company mainly engaged in waterworks plant manufacture. James Simpson, 1799–1869, the fourth son of Thomas Simpson, was a distinguished engineer and a contemporary of Thomas Telford and James Watt. Working for his father's company, he developed and perfected the sand bed water filter, which became the standard method of filtering water to make it drinkable. At least one of these filters is still in use today.

The original factory was at Grosvenor Road in London, but following the acquisition of a licence to manufacture the American Worthington pumps and engines, the company was in need of a room to expand.

The family had sporting connections (duck shooting) in Grantham and a site was considered there, but the raised bed of the Great Northern Railway through the town precluded the addition of a factory siding. Sites at Newark were considered: the site finally occupied by Ransome's and later a site in Balderton with the possibility of a siding from the GNR Leicester branch line.

The factory at Balderton opened in 1899, the erecting shop being built in 1911. The main use was the erection of the company's larger engines and pumps. The building contained underfloor water tanks for pressure testing and had a wooden block floor to protect large castings. The railway siding with the GWR was directly linked through the foundry via a pair of large doors in the west wall. The largest products

Aerial view of Worthington Simpson's site.

Triple-expansion steam pumps at the Kempton Park Great Engine Trust.

Triple-expansion pumps.

to be assembled in there were the triple expansion pumping engines destined for the Metropolitan Water Board works at Kempton Park and were used to distribute raw water around the various reservoirs of the London area. The engines were installed in 1929. They were the largest engines of their type in the country. The engines are now in the care of the Kempton Great Engines Trust and one engine can be viewed in steam on bank holidays.

The shop continued to be used for large products after the Second World War when the company produced heat exchange equipment for the new large electricity power stations then being built by CEGB. W-S had developed welded construction of these large pieces of equipment rather than the earlier cast-iron method.

The swansong was perhaps in 1975: three large 60" sump pumps for dry dock duties for the Hyundai company in South Korea. The main thrust of the company's business had become batch production of small standard water pumps and a large building of the size of the erecting shop was difficult to justify. It was finally demolished as the factory was reduced in size and scope as a result of a series of takeovers.

During the Second World War, part of the factory was turned over to the assembly of field guns. Thereafter the workshop involved was always known as the Gun Shop.

A Worthington Simpson pump.

Tracing Office at Simpson's.

Field gun – made during the Second World War.

Water pumps in use.

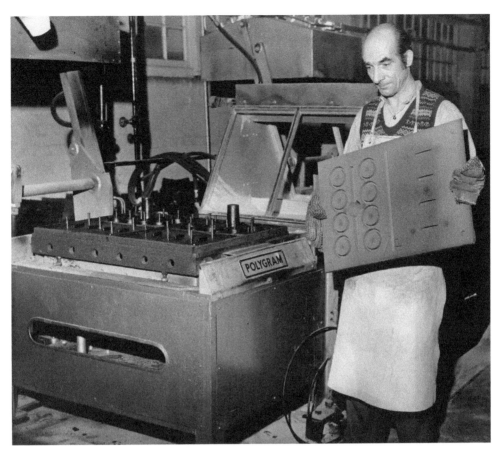

Foundry worker at Worthington Simpson.

Windmills

Two tower mills still stand without sails around the town as survivors of a once common means of obtaining free energy. Now windmills are again being erected in a more modern form to generate electricity.

The two surviving mills are Strays Mill at Farndon, where the A46 relief road crosses the Trent, and Coddington Mill on the crest of the Beacon Hill ridge between Coddington and Balderton.

Tower mills have survived because of their strong brick towers; however, there were other mills constructed of wood called post mills. In a post mill the whole mill body rotated to face the wind, not just the cap, as in a tower mill. One such mill existed in the woodyard between Bowbridge Road and Hatton Gardens, its plot currently occupied by a nursing home. Three such other mills were situated on the top of Beacon Hill in the area of the Beacon Heights housing estate, clearly situated to catch the steady wind from across the river valley.

Post mills could be relocated but were also susceptible to fire. Consequently, very few have survived.

A post mill seen in the background.

An oil painting of a post mill on Tolney Lane, painted by the artist Henry Dawson (1811–78) in 1840.

Parnham's Mill

Many people in Newark can remember Parnham's watermill off Millgate. As well as being a distinctive local landmark, it was (until its destruction by fire in 1965) an important survivor from the time of Britain's Industrial Revolution.

Parnham's Mill.

Parnham's Mill from the River Trent (seen in the background).

Mill being demolished.

The mill was built in the late eighteenth century and, for most of its life, was concerned with the production of flour. It was originally erected, however, for the spinning of cotton, taking advantage of the great trade in that commodity opened up by (Sir) Richard Arkwright's invention of the water frame.

In 1771, Arkwright had opened a factory at Cromford in Derbyshire, finding a ready market for his cotton thread among the well-established weaving trade in Manchester. Over succeeding years, many other cotton-spinning factories were opened, with the number increasing still further after 1785 when the High Court ruled against Arkwright in his attempts to restrict the exploitation of his machine by unregistered users.

In the light of this, it is perhaps significant that the first intentions to build a cotton mill at Newark have been dated to a period just two years after Arkwright's unsuccessful court case. The Duke of Newcastle owned the land on which the cotton mill was built, and during 1787 a number of bills for the establishment of a brickyard were sent to him by a so-called cotton mill company. In the following year, some 50,000 bricks were brought to the site, all of which were paid for by the duke.

Timber for the building, meanwhile, was supplied by Messrs Handley and Sketchley of Newark (timber merchants), who were also partners in the cotton mill venture. Samuel Sketchley had come to Newark from Burton-on-Trent, and in around 1766 established Newark's first brewery on the town wharf.

He entered partnership with William Handley – a successful local banker – in the 1770s, and their brewery later evolved into what became Warwick's and Richardson's on Northgate.

By 1790, construction of the cotton mill would appear to have been largely complete: it is shown on William Attenburrow's map of Newark published in that year, and in the following year (1791) the *Universal British Directory* clearly records the business of Sketchley, Handley, Jessop and Marshall, cotton manufacturers, as operating on Millgate.

Of particular interest among the list of partners is William Jessop who, prior to his involvement with the cotton mill, had risen to become one of the country's foremost civil engineers and canal builders. He was chief engineer on the Grand Union Canal and worked on the Cromford Canal for Sir Richard Arkwright in Derbyshire.

William Jessop lived in Newark from 1784 to 1805 in a house directly opposite the old police station on Appletongate. He was Mayor of Newark in 1790 and 1803.

In view of Jessop's expertise in canal construction, it is tempting to speculate whether part of his involvement with the cotton mill concerned designing or supervising its water-management scheme. The mill as originally built in the 1780s was five storeys high and thirteen bays wide with (it is thought) initially two waterwheels rated at 50hp each. It was used exclusively for the spinning of cotton thread, which was then transported by water to the great weaving factories in Manchester. There is no evidence of cotton cloth ever having been produced at the Newark mill.

At the height of its production, the mill is said to have employed around 300 people, mainly women and children who earned between one shilling and five shillings a week. William Dickinson in his *History of Newark*, first published in 1806 (p137), mentions that the mill provided employment for many of the town's poorest families, and an official report on Newark's workhouse in 1797 notes that of the twenty child inmates, ten went out daily to work at the cotton mill.

Close to the factory itself, meanwhile, Cotton Square – a yard of seventeen houses on the east side of Millgate almost opposite Mill Lane – is sometimes said to have provided homes for workers at the mill. There is certainly some evidence to suggest that they were erected around the same time as the mill, although the occupations of its original householders is not known.

After a profitable existence of over twenty years, cotton manufacture at the Newark mill ceased in the early nineteenth century.

By 1820 (according to R. P. Shilton's *History of Newark* p540) only one of the original partners – Marshall – was still involved with the mill and by 1822 Pigot's Directory records it as having passed into the hands of James Thorpe & Son, corn merchants and flour millers.

From this time onwards the mill was used exclusively for the production of flour. Thorpe extended the original building in 1835 (adding a third waterwheel), and in

1850 adapted the mechanism for steam power. It was taken over by Parnham's in 1886, in whose hands it remained until the disastrous fire of 1965. All that remains today are the footings, the wheel wells and the millpond.

Other watermills existed on the river making use of the power available. One such mill, a timber-sawing one, was located on the opposite side of the weir to Parnham's mill, but is again merely footings on the riverbank.

Mineral Railways

Newark boasted a large gypsum mining enterprise to the south-east of the town. This quarrying was served by a narrow gauge railway, which transported its produce to Spring Wharf on the Trent (now behind Newark Marina). The tramway dated to around the 1840s and was built by Messrs Wilson & Robinson, who ran the gypsum and clay quarries before they were taken over by Cafferata & Co. in 1882.

The line crossed the Fosse Way just below the Spring House pub and had a small brick building to house the crossing keeper. There were no gates, just a man with a red flag who directed the steam locomotive to cross the road.

This railway ran up until the early 1950s and ran behind the gardens of houses in Devon Road. The embankment for the line can still be seen crossing Devon Park.

For many years the building was used as a sweet shop.

Railway Viaduct over the Trent

Until the 1950s, the railway was the most usual method of transporting large loads. Consequently, factories manufacturing large items were located near to the railway. (See chapter on Worthington Simpson Ltd.)

A railway viaduct over the River Trent.

The concentration of industry north-east of the town between the Fosse Way, River Trent and the East Coast line was served by a joint line from the Midland line crossing the river on a bridge and curving round to join the Great Northern Railway line. A simpler later loop, still in use, was used to link the Midland Railway to the Great Northern line just north of the station.

The Viaduct had brickwork approaches, a central pillar in the middle of the river and a steel span and was constructed in the later part of the nineteenth century.

The industries consisted of the brewing, malting, boiler and glue works.

Maltings

Malt begins as grain, usually barley, which begins germinating with the addition of water and heat (steeping). After this initiation of germination, it is allowed to continue in a controlled environment, with constant turning, until drying arrests the process. The barley is then malted and ready for brewing.

Originally malting and brewing was a domestic process but with increasing populations and demand the process was industrialised.

The drinking of ale and beer was part of normal life as a means to have a safe fluid intake. Before filtration and purification began in the nineteenth century, most water was unfit to drink. Beer, in its small beer or diluted form, was widely used as an alternative form of refreshment by children and servants.

Newark, because of its location in the Trent Valley, with its wide spaces for farming and good water supply from wells, was an ideal location for brewing and malting. Larger malthouses spread along the river as it flowed northwards out of the town, the river providing both transport links and the means to remove the waste.

Baird's Maltings.

Peaches Maltings.

Maltings' fire.

Maltings (Gilstrap Earp & Co.) after the fire.

The main maltster was William Gilstrap, who later became a baronet.

The Newark method of floor malting, with its huge demand of labour, could not be made more efficient, and gradually more mechanized methods were introduced in new maltings built nearer to the barley fields, for example in Louth, Lincolnshire. The buildings were substantial and some became warehouses and workshops. An industry of pine furniture production arose for a short time at the end of the twentieth century, using both the buildings and initially the stripped-out pinewood from the floors. The main reason for the loss of buildings was the floor height (approximately 6ft) that did not enable them to be converted to accommodation. Some of the buildings, however, were consumed in spectacular fires that could be seen from several miles away and were often considered locally to be arson for insurance purposes.

Cattle Market

The Cattle Market site in the Castle Grounds had been given to the town earlier in the 1880s by William Gilstrap as part of his gift of a library, with the intention that the land would provide a stipend for a librarian. It was thought desirable however that the land become a garden and, to this end, the Viscountess Ossington offered £1,200 on condition that the site was 'laid out, planted, improved and maintained, for the purpose of being used by the public, free in perpetuity, as public walks and pleasure grounds'.

Cattle market in the castle grounds.

The cattle market in 1989 – over the river.

Cattle market, 1990.

This gift was bolstered by a sum of £500 from Alderman Henry Branston, leaving a sum of £2,500 to be raised by the town to complete the purchase of the desired area.

The castle and the Crown property embracing the ground lying between the ruins and Castle Gate was acquired in 1889, and architect Henry Ernest Milner (around 1845–1906) was called in to landscape the site. The Castle Gardens were opened on Queen Victoria's seventieth birthday in May of that year, and have remained a public park ever since. The park was renovated in 2000 using a grant from the Heritage Lottery Fund. The Cattle Market was moved to Tolney Lane after the park's opening, where it remained for around 100 years before moving over the railway line.

Scales Row – The Scales Factory

George Scales established his linen factory on Farndon road just outside the town and alongside the River Devon in the late eighteenth century. He also used the 'pure mineralized water of the spring 'St Catherine's well', which is within the grounds. There was also the added advantage of space for processes and development and good communications. There was a ready market for some products. The factory produced linen cloth, which was made into the distinctive Newark smocks, usually dyed blue. These were used to clothe local agricultural workers.

With the opening of the Trent and Mersey Canal in 1777, there was transport for raw materials that came directly from Lancashire.

Mr Scales' factory brought into his control a process that had been domestic in the past, with the spinning and weaving processes taking place in cottages in the surrounding villages, and the finished product brought in by 'factors' – hence the term factory.

Close by the factory, a row of houses was specially built for the workers to live in and produce the cloth. They were of distinctive design with an elevated ground floor over a half-buried cellar with windows where the man of the house would do the weaving while the ladies would spin in the house proper. The ground-floor living area was reached by a series of steps, giving the cottages their local name of the 'Step Houses'.

Of Mr Scales' factory, the only surviving remnant is his own fine Georgian house (Orchard House).

Scales linen factory's letterhead.

Aerial view of the Scales factory site.

Scales Row, Farndon Road.

Scales Row, 1958.

A man's smock.

Boy wearing a smock.

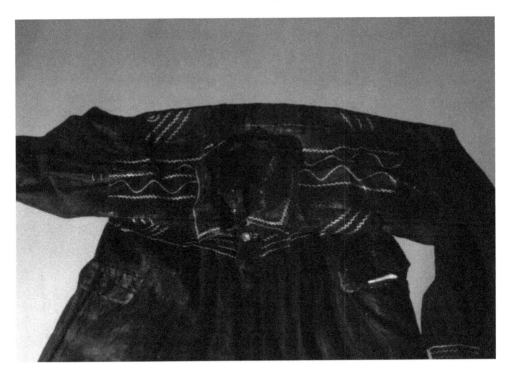

Detail on a smock.

Scales factory being demolished.

Victoria Street Smithy

At the corner of Regent Street and Victoria Street was the smithy of Mr J. E. Sibcy, reputed to be the town's last blacksmith.

In the days before internal combustion engines, all transport, both personal and goods, was horse drawn. This meant that a large number of farrier/blacksmiths would be required to service both the horses and the carriages or carts.

Blacksmiths work by heating pieces of wrought iron or steel until the metal becomes soft enough for shaping with hand tools, such as a hammer, anvil and chisel. Heating generally takes place in a forge fuelled by coal, charcoal or coke.

Historically, the jobs of farrier and blacksmith were practically synonymous, shown by the etymology of the word: farrier comes from Middle French *ferrier* (blacksmith), from the Latin word *ferrum* (iron). A farrier's work would have included shoeing horses, as well as the fabrication and repair of tools, the forging of architectural pieces, and so on. Modern-day farriers usually specialize in horseshoeing, focusing their time and effort on the care of the horse's hoof.

In some instances, the farrier side of the business survived and now serves the horse-riding community, often mobile; in other cases the blacksmithing side evolved into a small engineering company or into creating decorative wrought-iron work.

Mr Sibcy's smithy existed into the middle of the twentieth century when it was demolished to make way for a supermarket.

Bookstall – Newark Covered-in Market

The stall was taken over by Mrs Southerington and finally by Turners, before the Market Hall was revamped.

Book stall in Newark's covered market.

Covered-in Market

Behind the Town Hall, leading through to Middlegate, is the Market Hall. It was constructed in 1884 at a cost of £2,500 on the site of the former butcher's shambles. The engraving shows the original sliding doors at the Middlegate end.

Newark's Royal Exchange shopping arcade, behind the Town Hall, recaptures much of the splendour that originally marked it as one of the town's great Victorian improvements. A foundation stone near the Middlegate entrance tells us the building was begun in October 1883, although the story of its construction goes back much further than that. In fact, the building of the Covered Market, as it was originally known, was simply the last in a long series of events that give this part of the town its colourful history. In 1798, almost 100 years before the market was built, the site behind the Town Hall was allocated for use as Newark's meat market, or 'butcher's shambles'. New buildings for the purpose were erected on the site and opened in 1799. Adjacent to the shambles and also fronting Middlegate was the town's theatre, which had been established by J. Brough in 1774. The theatre and shambles continued side by side until 1882, when the Urban Sanitary Authority began investigating alternative sites for the butchers' market. As things stood, the mere location of the shambles, with its extensive displays of raw meat, could make for a most unpleasant atmosphere for the Town Hall (directly above) on hot days. Moreover, the authority expressed concern about the state of disrepair and untidiness into which the shambles had been allowed to descend. Newark's MP, W. N. Nicholson, considered the whole area nothing short of a scandal, while the mayor, Robert Henry, described the buildings as simply a miserable tumble of dens. Not wishing to lose the retail aspect completely, the sanitary authority proposed that the site be taken over by a covered market dedicated purely to the sale of groceries and poultry. By August 1882, a competition for designing the new structure had been held and won by Mr C. Bell, FRIBA, of London. Tenders were invited and accepted from local firms such as C. Baines (£1,390) for the general building work, and Abbott & Co. (£383) for the ironwork of the roof and the slender, ornate pillars, which still support the structure today. Things appeared to be going smoothly until negotiations opened for clearance and purchase of the site. Although a part was already owned by the corporation, other parcels remained in the hands of local charities – those of Brown and Philpot. Reaching satisfactory agreements with these bodies caused a delay of the best part of a year. It was not until 29 October 1883 that the mayor, in a short ten-minute ceremony, was able to set work in motion by laying the foundation stone. Following the demolition of the shambles and adjoining theatre, the new structure was finally built in October 1884, at a cost of around £3,000. The opening ceremony took place on the 13th of that month under the auspices of the mayor, Alderman Gascoyne, accompanied by the markets committee and local MPs. 'The building', noted the *Newark Advertiser* in its subsequent report of the event,

has a very commodious appearance. The iron span roof is lofty and is supported by elegant but powerful iron pillars standing on stone corbels. The interior is of white brick and the floor is of concrete. The roof is of wood, boarded, and the exterior slated in. A long range of windows in the roof on the north side admits plenty of light in the daytime, while at night the building will be illuminated with two large Brays lamps of seven lights each, and four gas lights round each pillar.

The original plan of the covered market is still readily identifiable today, although it is interesting to recall some features that were proposed but never carried out. Among these, and integral to Bell's design, was a plan to use the upper storey or gallery as a public lecture hall. Newark's MP, W. N. Nicholson, was particularly in favour of this aspect of the scheme, and remarked that it made provision for the supply of food for the mind, whereas the market below concentrated on food for the body. The lecture room, of course, was never built, yet even without this facility there appeared no room for doubt among those present at the opening ceremony that the market would prove a great boon to the town. The air of euphoria, however, did not appear to infect one local commentator who, a few years after the opening, turned a highly satirical eye on the success of the new venture. 'Few towns', he wrote,

possess buildings other than of a denominational character wherein the tired wayfarer may retire from the busy scenes of life for serene self-contemplation assured of isolation in the midst of commonplace distractions. Newark, however, is happy in this respect. The large and commodious new market hall, built for business which never came, offers at once seclusion and a perfect quietude and atmosphere of repose, around which the town's trade and commerce runs without disturbing the solitary interior.

Deep food for thought indeed!

5. Ecclesiastical Buildings

Christianity was undoubtedly present around Newark in the time of the later Roman Empire and until the time of the Anglo-Saxons, but paganism would have taken its place, as evidenced by the large area of cremation burials in the Millgate area of the town.

The Viking occupation after the ninth century would also be pagan, but later there was some evidence of late Saxon Christian burial rites in the area of the castle.

It is in the castle that the earliest Christian chapel is to be found. Dr John Samuels and Pamela Marshall established its location in the inner bailey in the major excavation. In addition, stones from a Romanesque four-order arch has been pieced together and can be seen restored in the Registration Office. This may indicate the scale of the structure. Its last recorded use was the marriage of Lady Elizabeth Manners to William Cecil, Lord Burley, in January 1589.

A Romanesque archway, constructed with stones found at the castle.

The earliest stone church on the site of the present town church was in the transitional style and only the crypt and four partial pillars at the crossing remain of this church. The building of the present church was interrupted by the Black Death and not completed until the fifteenth century in the early English style.

The pattern of Christianity in the town was then typical of any medieval town except for the large number of chantries, which reflect the wealth of the town rather than its religiosity.

The rise of the nonconformists produced a number of churches/chapels in the extended eighteenth- and nineteenth-century town. In addition, the fight back by the established church resulted in a number of daughter churches being established in the same areas. Several of these still exist but are reused as dwellings or commercial properties.

Newark's Old Rectorial Tithe Barn

Situated on Lovers Lane, the old rectorial tithe barn was demolished in 1960. A housing development known as Tithe Barn Court now stands on the site. Although the tithe barn ended its life on Lovers Lane, it is worth noting that being outside Newark's medieval boundaries, this cannot have been its original location.

An ordination issued by the Archbishop of York in 1426 discussing the apportionment of tithes in Newark implies that the barn was then located a little way to the north of the parish church of St Mary Magdalene, roughly in the area now occupied by the Mount C of E Primary School. Despite demolition, some timbers from the tithe barn still survive and samples taken in 1996 by Drs Bob Laxton and Cliff Litton and Mr Robert Howard of the University of Nottingham's Tree Ring Dating Laboratory have revealed a construction date for the Newark Tithe Barn of around 1430.

Although originally held by the incumbent of Newark parish for the collection and storage of his rectorial tithes, following the Dissolution of the monasteries in the sixteenth century, the rights to collect such tithes in Newark was sold to a succession of local landowners. By the 1830s, the Newark Tithe Barn had become part of the farm owned by Mr G. A. Lacy. His stackyard was located at the corner of Queen's Road and Appletongate.

In 1957, the tithe barn and its surrounding area were acquired by compulsory purchase by Newark Town Council. As part of its scheme to rid Newark of slum housing, the council decided that owing to 'deterioration beyond preservation' the tithe barn had to be demolished. Attempts to save the ancient structure by dismantling it and re-erecting it elsewhere were made by local campaigners – one such scheme even proposed offering it to the City Museum in Newark, New Jersey, although the cost of shipping the pieces across to the USA ultimately proved prohibitive.

The barn was demolished in May 1960 (its last ignoble used having been as a depot for delivery lorries belonging to British Road Services, with the first residents of the new slats built in Tithe Barn Court, moving in the following March). The individual timbers of the barn were, however, saved and acquired by a local landowner who had plans to re-erect the barn as part of a private house on Beacon Heights in Newark. Little came of this plan, although the timbers remained on Beacon Hill in Newark until the mid-1970s.

Newark's tithe barn.

Interior of tithe barn.

Two views of Newark's tithe barn.

Tithe barn being demolished.

The Bede Houses

In the sixteenth century, three important charities were established in the town: the Magnus schools charity, Brown's charity and Philpott's charity. This latter charity initially provided for five men too old or infirm to work to be housed in the charity property in Coddington Lane, named Bede House Lane.

The charity's income was supplied by rents from properties in the town and local villages of Farndon, Stoke and Muskham.

The charity was administered by the alderman and his assistants, the vicar and two other elected townsmen. In 1738, the provision was enlarged to provide for fifteen persons, five of whom were to be women having the additional responsibility of washing and mending for the men. The mayor and aldermen were tasked with ensuring that there was 'no improper intercourse between the men and women'.

Further enlargement of the properties allowed for a final population of twenty-four, but by 1959 there was only one resident left.

In the early 1960s, the houses were pulled down and replaced by modern accommodation. The chapel, however, was retained and used as an office for a voluntary organization until recently when it has become an Odinist temple.

Newark's Bede Houses.

The Bede Houses being demolished.

Drawing of Newark's Spital (on Northgate).

St Leonard's Spital

The oldest almshouse still in existence is St Leonard's Hospital in Newark. The hospital was leased in 1609 to Sir William Cecil, Lord Burley (afterwards Earl of Exeter), grandson of William Cecil, Queen Elizabeth I's chief minister who carried out extensive building work and renamed it Exeter House and was known as 'the Spital'.

On the death of Earl of Exeter in 1642, the Dowager Countess built a house on Northgate with 1 acre of ground enclosed by a brick or stone wall enclosing an orchard or garden and known as Hospital House of St Leonard's. This was burned down during the Civil War, to protect the town from the Parliamentary forces.

In 1888, the old building in Northgate was pulled down and replaced by six comfortable homes endowed by Joseph Richardson with a house at either end for a 'deserving married couple to reside in during old age'.

St Leonard's Church

In the nineteenth century the population of the town increased threefold. Much of this new population was housed to the north of the town in the main malting area. At this time all of the denominations were expanding their mission to these areas.

The Church of England decided to create a new parish of St Leonard's to serve this area. The church was built of stone with a nave, chancel and side aisles seating 600 people on a site opposite that of the St Leonard's Spital. After building, many bequests and donations were given to embellish the building with stained glass and an impressive triptych with an alabaster centrepiece depicting the crucifixion.

Church of St Leonard, Northgate.

The chancel at St Leonard's Church.

St Leonard's Church being demolished.

Towards the turn of the century, the church, together with others in the area, came under the influence of the Oxford movement, an Anglo-Catholic section of the Church of England. The church then continued in this vein of churchmanship for much of the twentieth century, the vicars traditionally addressed as 'Father'.

In the late twentieth century, it was apparent that the potential congregation had moved away from this part of the town to the area north of the railway. It was therefore decided to relocate the church to serve this population with a combined church and community centre. The old church was closed on 5 November 1978 and the congregation walked in procession to the new church. Some items of church furniture were moved to the new building but the building was demolished. The remaining fittings and the site were sold.

St Augustine's Chapel
This chapel of ease of the Church of St Mary Magdalene was on Newton Street. The cornerstone of the new Mission Room and school was laid on 16 March 1886 and it opened on 22 July. The walls are of red brick, with concrete roof tiles. Above the

entrance (straight off the pavement) is a mock Tudor gable end with large four-light windows. All windows are plain.

The church consisted of a nave, chancel, apse, vestry, and organ chamber. The bell housing above the vestry was demolished in the 1970s and the bell, hung in 1919, was sent to a mission in South Africa. It had plain walls inside, painted pale blue or white latterly. There was a blue semicircular arch built into the chancel, but the chancel was white. The seating at first was on chairs, but nineteenth-century benches replaced them with poppy heads from the parish church. The choir stalls were in the chancel until the 1950s when they were taken into the nave. There was an oak communion rail and a dark oak reredos was acquired in 1915. A wooden lectern was donated in the 1970s. The pulpit was painted blue and white.

New pictures were donated for the bare walls in the early years. In later years, the only wall fittings were a Roll of Honour 1914–18 and a Cross of Nails by Robert Kiddey.

Originally there was a harmonium, then an electric organ in 1958, replaced in 1964 with a second-hand one. William Becher Tidd Pratt was the choirmaster from 1906 to 1956; the choir was known as 'Tidd Pratt's Angels'.

The building was used as a day school for three- to seven-year-olds until 1908 when the council school was built.

The chapel was threatened with demolition in 1993, but after protests the council agreed to a conversion to six dwellings, retaining the frontage and merely demolishing the vestry. It closed for Christian worship in May 1998.

St Augustine's chapel on Barnby Gate/Newton Street.

St Augustine's chancel.

St Augustine's chapel.

Holy Trinity Catholic Church

From the time of King Henry VIII until the Emancipation Act of 1829, it was forbidden in this country to practise Roman Catholicism. Throughout this time the religion was kept alive illegally in secret but the early bloody persecution was gradually relaxed until it re-emerged in the nineteenth century. Another factor in the re-emergence was the large numbers of Irish workers attracted by the digging of canals and the construction of railways. This would have increased the Catholic population of towns such as Newark.

To serve this population, a church was built at the Millgate end of Parliament Street. Externally the church resembled a typical small medieval church with a nave and square bell tower. Internally, however, there was no chancel just an apse for the altar.

The church was in the national news for the lying in state of General Sikorsky, the leader of exiled Poles in the Second World War who was killed in an air crash on Gibraltar. Winston Churchill delivered a eulogy at his funeral held in Westminster Cathedral. The general was buried in Newark's Polish cemetery, which he had opened only two years before. When Poland became free after the Cold War he was returned to his homeland in accordance with his wishes.

On 14 September 1993, his remains were exhumed and transferred via Polish Air Force TU-154M, and escorted by RAF 56 Sqn Tornado F3 jets, to the royal crypts at Wawel Castle in Kraków, Poland.

On this occasion the requiem mass was held in the parish church of St Mary Magdalene in the presence of Philip, Duke of Edinburgh. This was the first Catholic mass celebrated in the church since the Reformation.

In 1979, the congregation moved to a new church complex on Boundary Road and the old church was demolished.

Holy Trinity Catholic Church and Hall, Parliament Street.

General Sikorsky's funeral parade.

General Sikorsky's coffin lying in state.

About the Authors

Mike Cox and Jill Campbell are both members of Newark Archaeological & Local History Society. Mike is Chairman and Jill is Secretary and Treasurer.

Authors of two previous Newark books with Amberley Publishing – *Newark Through Time* and *Secret Newark*, this third book hopes to complete Newark's story.

Both have been involved in the promotion of Newark's history, and are actively involved in a range of activities, namely slide/tape presentations to various groups, conducting town tours, and also, since 1973, the erection of plaques around the town commemorating well-known people or buildings. These have been recognised by the English Heritage Blue Plaque Scheme.

The authors: Mike Cox and Jill Campbell.

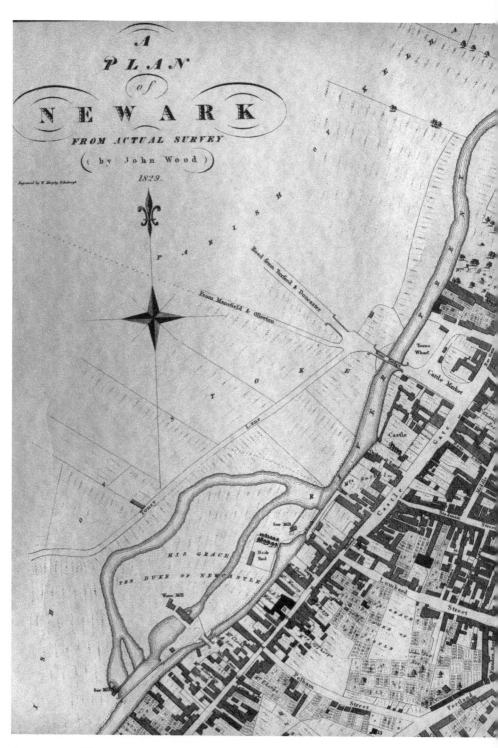

An 1829 rateable street plan of Newark by John Wood, Overseer to the Poor.

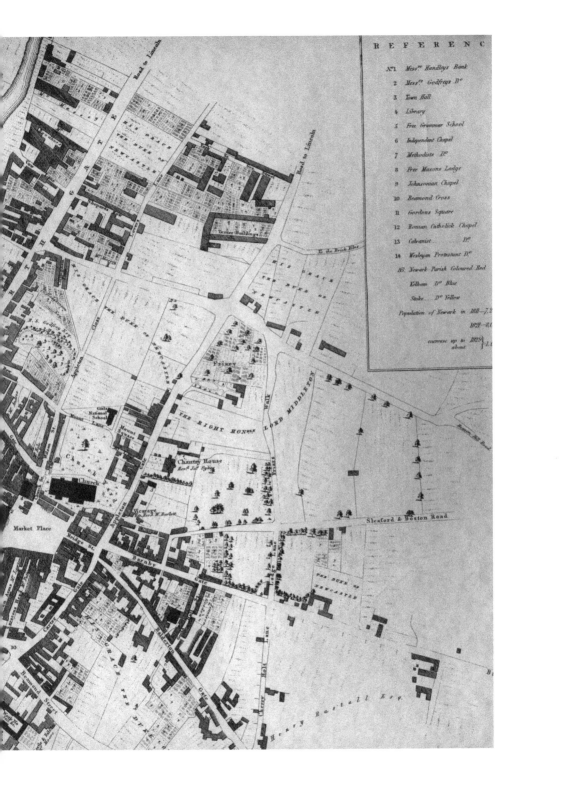

Road to Lincoln

Road to Lincoln

Yates Buildings

R. S. Godfreys

Girls
National School
Mount
Lane

Mount
Square

Church

Church

Market Place

Vicarage
Ms Rev.ᵈ W. Barlett

THE RIGHT HON.ᵇˡᵉ LORD MIDDLETON

Chantry House
Rev.ᵈ J.ᵒ Tyley

Walk

Beacon Hill Road

Sleaford & Boston Road

Friary

Barnby
Gate

Beamond Street

Holt Lane

Cherry Lane

Henry Rastall Esq.

Also Available from Amberley Publishing

This fascinating selection of photographs traces some of the many ways in which Newark has changed and developed over the last century.

Paperback
180 illustrations
96 pages
978-1-84868-567-3

Available from all good bookshops or to order direct
please call **01453-847-800**
www.amberley-books.com